To Helen & Sigmund Cohen —
        with all my
thanks for your
kindness — I hope you
find something of the N.Y.
we all love so much
in the following pages —

                        Very
                        Julius Horwitz

THE CITY

JULIUS HORWITZ

THE CITY

THE WORLD PUBLISHING COMPANY

CLEVELAND AND NEW YORK

Library of Congress Catalog Card Number: 53–6632

FIRST EDITION

HC 753

Copyright 1953 by Julius Horwitz

To Lois

THE AUTHOR wishes to thank the editors of *Commentary* magazine for permission to include "New York" (originally "New York—1950"), "The Conspirators," "A Cup of Tea," "The Campaign" and "The Generations of Man," which first appeared in their pages. He also wishes to thank the *Jewish Frontier* for permission to include "The Strudel."

He wishes to express particular appreciation to Clement Greenberg for his kind help.

Contents

When my aunt first came to New York she cried, "Look! New York is like a roomful of pearls. What does one single pearl mean?"

We live together in a community, and this book, both its fictional and non-fictional pages, is the story of New York as I have known it, a community of people who are neither more nor less than any other sons of God.

THE CITY

New York

THE FIRST DOORBELL I RANG WAS ANSWERED BY AN OLD widowed Negro woman who lived alone on the top floor of a red-brick office building in the financial district of Manhattan. It was Saturday morning, the first day of the mid-century census. The old Negro woman made me feel that the happiest people in the world are old widowed Negro women with just enough money to live on and reasonably comfortable places to live in, and who aren't afraid of the end of life. Perhaps they're lonely, and sometimes they may ask: did God do all this and why? But still she seemed to be the happiest person I had seen in a long time. And, past seventy, she looked for work, kept house, and wanted to make sure that the government got everything correct about her.

Around the corner from her musty Victorian apartment, under the Third Avenue El, and farther east, close to the river, lived the handful of people that were left of the once densely inhabited downtown New York. The women stay on, eighty years old, seventy, living on the top floors of office buildings, cleaning for a living —or rather for rent— and afraid to move elsewhere; others have been charwomen in the financial district for so long that they feel it's home and hang on to the few remaining habitable buildings. These are cold-water flats, no toilets, no tubs, dirty, dilapidated, the El roaring past the living room windows, no community, nothing but the curiously exciting daytime

15

streets of the financial district. The people had to be tracked down, literally one by one, to their sunless, cold, ugly apartments. Under the El, two tenements, side by side, but for whole blocks no people. One man alone in a room that one can enter only through a public toilet. Another man living in the very upper tip of a skyscraper, so that you had to reach his apartment by climbing a circular staircase.

At first Greenwich Village seemed to be filled with wives separated from husbands, husbands separated from wives, and beautiful girls separated from their families. It's probably correct to say that Greenwich Village has the highest percentage of divorced people in America for a community where divorce isn't a special product, as in Reno, and possibly the highest percentage of attractive girls for a community where beauty isn't a special cult, as in Hollywood. In a single block you run the gamut of urban living. Going from door to door, being admitted *carte blanche*, seeing from one building to the next the extreme diversities in taste, education, income, and housing, is like taking a sociology course in a roller coaster. Nowhere else in the world, I suspect, can you experience anything similar. You begin with a tenement, dark, dank, inhabited by low-income families, growling voices, family arguments, old wasted men, and then to a rooming house, cubicles holding copywriters, models, commercial artists, typists, radio writers, salesgirls, students, cooks, waiters, dancers, artists—and then next door is a town house, one family to five stories, rich old American family, beautiful furniture that would bring a high price at auction; then a large apartment house, twenty families, seven rooms to a family, big, square, roomy; and then a row of converted brownstones, housing writers, teachers, clerks, secretaries, a lead in a Broadway show, a singer, more houses, more professions, and then, two tenements, Irish and Italian intermingled, end the street.

How do they live? Reproductions from the Museum of Modern Art on the wall. Van Gogh is the favorite. An occasional Toulouse-Lautrec. A fake Renoir. Few originals. Dogs of all breeds. Studio couches dominate. Books, rows of books. Records. Black walls, red walls—burlap walls. Square ordinary flats furnished with install-ment-plan furniture. Enormous oversized rooms. North skylights. Easels ten feet high. Pianos. Miserable little rooms with a bed, a dresser, a chair. Toilet in the hallway for three people. Blond oak furniture. Conspicuous investments to be modern. Just everything thrown together. No pattern. Some come off. Others make you feel so sorry for the people that you want to say, look, leave Manhattan, go home, stop trying so hard, it isn't worth it, Iowa must be a wonderful place to live in. No living in sin. The census doesn't recognize sin. A man and woman together are to be recognized as husband and wife. Salesgirls from Macy's having a party. "Hello! Look who's here. The census taker. The census taker! Look, he's a real census taker. Are you a real census taker?"

With some people you talk. A famous professor of anthropology whose little daughter wants to be in on her first census. A psychologist who never read Tolstoy. A radio announcer who is bursting to tell you that he makes $10,000 a year. A dress designer who makes $13,000 and you wonder how. A little man in tweeds with a high piping voice who insists there is no form devised to record his personality. "Look, don't ask me any more questions, there are some people you just can't census."

The girls. Nobody ever seems to see the girls in Greenwich Village. Only a handful invade the neighborhood bars. But the rest remain forever in their rooms. Two girls from Nebraska sharing a flat. Editorial workers on a magazine. Copywriters. Advertising assistants. Research workers. Scriptwriters. Teachers. Young, sleek, college-trained girls. But so lonely. One girl in a black dress, chalk face, body limp, room dirty, repeating over and over again: "I'm going home in the fall. I think I'm going home. I don't like it here. I think I'm going home."

You can spot the rich girls. They never complain about the rent. But the working girls. They gripe. And they talk. They seem to be anxious to talk to somebody. A man in their apartment. But no sex. Only offers of beer. The models. Who ever sees a model but a photographer? One and a half rooms. A modern webbed chair. How little money they earn. Rent to pay. New clothes. Supper. Breakfast. Phone bills. Carfare. Income. One thousand. Two thousand. Three thousand is high. You begin to think that life is complete if you can *only* make four thousand a year. The girls are so damn pretty. Why don't they go home? Marry the richest boy in town. Live in a detached house with fruit trees and a white fence. One girl permits the top of her breasts to show. "Tell them the bastard landlord is getting too much for this hole. Eighty-five dollars a month. What do I think the apartment is worth unfurnished? Thirty dollars. That's all. Thirty dollars." It's a great question. "Is your apartment furnished or unfurnished? If it is furnished what do you think the unfurnished rent should be?" It's the only opportunity to express yourself on the census form. And the girls yell the loudest. Their fields are all jammed. Editorial assistants, copywriters, receptionists, actresses, models, all low-paid, dozens of girls to pounce on every vacancy. But they pay the Village rents so life will be a little less empty.

One girl, an actress, makes the world stand still. A blonde, who uncomfortably gives you the feeling that the world is ice cream and cake and you're an idiot not to realize it. A comic-book princess, perfectly formed, lovely, but as innocent of the world as a cellophane-wrapped lollypop. How much did you earn last year? "Golly, I don't know. Will it be all right to call my lawyer?" Certainly. "Hello, lawyer. How much did I make last year?" An astronomical figure. Next door the rent is five dollars a week and itinerant Italian cooks and waiters come and go.

One street makes you so nervous that it's a task to record the answers. A dirty, ugly, short little street. The inevitable dull red brick. From outside the appearance of a town house. Inside: no lights, broken wooden stairs. Most of the people you talk to in the Village have a vague or real understanding of what one is up against for the sake of living in most of the available Village apartments. But in this house the people are just trapped. They have no place else to go. The parlor floor is sealed off. Three rents for one. The first room contains a husband, his wife, four infants, in a space twelve feet by fifteen. No bath. No toilet. Shared. High rent. The next room has an ornate old bed and an ornate old woman. Upstairs, men half undressed, beds unmade, dirty shirts, dark hallways; upstairs again, on the top, a small room, a big bed, a big chest, a small bed, a husband, wife, two infants, a 100-watt bulb. Next house, railroad flats, five dark rooms, one old lady has five rooms, she lets out four rooms, won't tell how much she pays for rent. Afraid to expose her greed. Heavy hanging drapes. The rotten odor of the used-to-be dollar whorehouses in Alliance, Ohio. The third house from the corner. People trying. Rooms painted. New furniture. Families. Clean-cut radio producers. Bright bubbling wives. A television set off pitch. An original painting on the wall. Rows of books. Classical records. And one room is so goddamn ugly you want to run out on it before your head splits open.

The Italians and the Irish form the bedrock of the Village. The Irish on the West Side. The Italians on all sides. They aren't transient, players on a checkerboard, like the girls from Indiana. They live in dilapidated flats on Bleecker Street, duplexes on Charles Street, clean, ordinary flats, make a living, a good living; but some don't hesitate to tell you: "The docks are rotten. Two days work a week. Break your back. How can you live? No, I don't know what my husband makes. Maybe two thousand. But then we get relief." The Irish dock-workers have the largest families and the most precarious incomes. The Irish and the Italians make up the bedrock. But the others from every state, including Wyoming, make up the Village. Greenwich Village. A community largely of strangers, who don't want to be strangers, who want to dance in the street, but instead find themselves in dreary flats, drinking bottled beer.

The East Fifties are supposed to be one of the most expensive neighborhoods in the world. It is also the poorest. On Second Avenue the landlords blocked off the railroad flats and converted each into separate units. One half rents for $11.00 a month; the half facing the sun for $16.00.

On the side streets that empty into Sutton Place the landlords converted the railroad flats into one-room modern studios, beds folding into couches, making a home for people who just can't get into Sutton Place but wouldn't think of living anywhere else; a curious *mélange* of salesladies, advertising writers, radio producers, investment agents, nurses, salesmen, actresses, people similar to those in the Village except they lack the *éclat*. These are the most lonely people in the world, I think.

The apartments are deserted until six. Everybody works. You have to, to pay the rent. One room. A bathroom. A kitchenette that hangs on the side of a wall. Sleek modern furniture, uncomfortable chairs. Cocktails. Highballs. The smell of gin in the hallways. What do you drink? If there were no cocktail to come home to, no telephone to pick up, the people living here would probably blow out their brains *en masse*. The incomes small. Not enough to cross the Avenue. The models may get a little of the dazzle. You walk in on a cocktail party. No laughter. The heavy drinking hasn't started yet. The hostess, absolutely lovely, a model, talks to you, low, sexy, still in her act. The one-room apartment is only temporary. Sutton Place is the goal. The tenants have the souls of the people around the corner, down the street. A few are married. But so many live alone. What are they after? Will you have a drink, what do you drink—oh, you're taking the census! Unbend, let loose. These are the people who never kept up with the Joneses. It's a relief to walk in on a human being. A *grande dame*, a regal old lady, money gone, magnificent face, the most sensible apartment on the street, living alone, and when I praise her maple sewing cabinet, she tells me what it means to be past seventy and ready to die.

On the top floor I almost caused a tragedy. A woman is entertaining a well-pressed, straight-haired man. She tries to avoid the interview. Please come another time, please. But it will only take a minute. Then the question about age. She hesitates. The man excuses himself from the room. Now he knows, she says in a panic, now he'll guess how old I am. I look at the bottle of Canadian Club on the cocktail table, the two glasses, the couch, her slim body, and I want to tell her, don't worry, he'll follow you, why in the hell do you think he's here? If these people lived anywhere else they would be the real middle class but in Manhattan they have nothing. One woman is hysterical when I knock on the door. God damn it, you would come tonight. I can't talk to you. And then I hear the quarrel inside. Her husband lost his job.

On Second Avenue, in the chopped-up cold-water flats, you find the people who have almost completely given up. No ties. Women alone, old, never married. Men, dirty, old, coming to the door in long underwear. The rooms are dark, sparsely furnished, and you get a sense of at last finding the end of the road, the last pretense of patterned living, before the Bowery, the asylums, death. The doors are all bolted. Some have heavy chains. You wonder what the people are guarding. The rooms smell. Some are genuinely perverse. From floor to ceiling, burlap bags of old clothes, newspapers, rags, blocking off the whole room except a little space for a stove and old musty chairs where three people sit eating barley soup while you ask: Did you work last week? If so, how many hours? What state were you born in? How old were you on your last birthday? As though it all made good solid sense.

In another room you linger. Books line the mantel. The first books you've seen since the Village. The room is bare except for a kitchen table and two chairs. The lights don't work. You look closer at the dusty books. Thoreau. Emerson. Kant. St. Augustine. Browning. Keats. Shelley. Plato. Lucretius. Spinoza. The little man, unshaven, in a dirty collarless shirt, waits for you to ask the work question: "I don't work. I quit working. On my last job, a dishwasher. I have just enough money to live on. I don't go to the movies. I don't listen to the radio. I read—who do you think was the greatest English poet?" It's a matter of taste, you say. "But just pick a man." All right, I like Shakespeare in *Hamlet*. "What do you think of Browning?" First rate. "What about St. Augustine? Do you know the *City of God?*" God is introduced. He is a churchman but he doesn't like the church. The philosophers didn't understand God, he tells me. I think they did, I tell him. "Who do you think has the finest style? I think Carlyle." I answer, I don't like to talk about style. But I like Swift. Style is the way a man feels, his mood, not a mechanical arrangement. He listens, agrees. But I have a thousand people to see. "Stay and talk," he urges. "Let's talk about St. Augustine. A good fleshy man." Some other time. "Come up any time." I will. Goodbye. And another room, the bolt sliding back, an Irish face out of a

Dublin saloon, a pinched, hollow woman sitting stiffly in the dark. The man, wait a minute, I'll put on the light. And he puts a match to the gaslight in the chandelier.

Sutton Place is around the corner. The loftiest living in the country.

Luftmenshen—and the others, coat manufacturers, shirt manufacturers, doctors, coat buyers, shirt buyers, dress buyers, importers, exporters, advertising executives, vice presidents, and the rich old ladies living on "$10,000-plus." The rich somehow seemed to pick up the phrase, "$10,000-plus," either from the newspapers or their lawyers. The "$10,000-plus" refers to the income question— from those who made less than $10,000 a year the exact amount of their income was required, but for the others "$10,000-plus" would do. And the $10,000-plusses *live*. Big, beautiful, spacious apartments, mechanically tightened together by interior decorators, sweeping views of Manhattan, bottles of expensive liquor on antique trays. It beats the Village. In Greenwich Village on a single block you can be sure of running the gamut of life, but here are the people who have licked the system.

The dress designer is busy spraying toilet water on the top of her breasts. "Am I married? No. I'm divorced. And I hope the bastard is dead." Why the language? Her apartment is the ultimate of the Manhattan fable. A penthouse. Early American furniture gives the impression of loot-hungry decorators making a raid on all the antique shops. An orgy of furniture. The woman is drunk in the apartment below. Everybody is drinking, but the woman is drunk. The man is trying to give me the right answers because he's here on a permanent visa and doesn't want to alienate the government. But the drunken woman keeps shouting: "He doesn't have a right coming in here. He doesn't have a right. He doesn't have a right. . . ." Downstairs the woman is waiting for cocktails. She is dressed for dinner. The apartment is "classic" American. Her husband comes in. A handsome boy. Stockbroker. Black silk umbrella. Black homburg. Black suit. The first thing he does is phone for whisky. Whisky is the pre-dinner drink. The post-dinner drink.

Heavy carpeting. A maid. A long leather bar. Tall polished glasses.

More booze. An enormous television set anchors the living room.
A beautiful regular-featured blonde on the couch. The man is big,
fat, old, a stockbroker. And the girls who don't know what they do
for a living, lush, in blue silk robes, who don't dare lie to the government, who live in apartments that actually look like Hollywood
sets. "Now tell me what you do for a living." "I'm a dancing teacher."
"Good. Now, how many hours did you teach last week?" "Oh—I
only teach over the weekend." "Well, how many hours?" "Oh!
You know what to put down. Be a good guy and say the right
thing."

You have to stop counting people every so often to hurry across
57th Street to the tavern on 58th for a glass of cold beer. It begins to
seem natural for people to pay $600 a month for a four-room
apartment. To have rooms filled with the most obviously expensive
stuff on the market. For television sets to pop out of elaborate
secretaries that fill the side of a long wall. For women to say, over
and over again, disdainfully: "I don't work. I've never worked."

One building, more than the others, seemed to house a particularly
solid concentration of flat, two-dimensional people of the twentieth
century. A few people are there by mistake, or housing necessity,
but the others seem to have come together by affinity.

One woman was definitely living in the house by error. At first
she wouldn't admit me. She had to call down to the lobby to find
out if I had been cleared by the doorman. "I'm sorry to have made
you wait. But you don't blame me. You can't trust people in this
neighborhood. Such funny people. Come in, come in. You look so
tired." She was wearing a cotton housecoat. "Sit down by the table.
Put your book on the table. Such a heavy book they make you carry
around. Let me get you a drink. Maybe you'd like some whisky?"
It was too hot for a drink of straight whisky but I said all right to
please her. She brought out a square bottle of twelve-year-old Scotch.
"A whole glass?" she asked. Just a little, please. And then she saw
me looking at the white tablecloth with a Hebrew prayer as its
design. "You're a Jewish boy, aren't you?" she said. "Tell me the
truth." I'm a Jewish boy, I told her, that's the truth. "A Jewish boy.
You know, I'm Jewish, too. I put the tablecloth out for my father-

in-law. He likes to be in a Jewish house. This building. I'd like to move away. The rent we pay." The living room was stuffed with furniture. Very expensive conservative-modern. And birdcages. Three singing birds. "I sit here all day. Nobody to talk to. You know, they have famous people living in this house. A girl who sings over the radio."

The house belongs to the people who can afford it—not to the young couple in a narrow one-and-a-half who can't even afford furniture because of the high rent—but to the producers, actresses, stage stars, slick writers, advertising executives, designers, publishers, art dealers, stockbrokers, financial advisers, and the real rich, the people who live on $10,000-plus, the people who sweep in money out of the air, who make the rest of us feel like damned fools. But sit and drink their booze, examine the arrangement of the furniture, the faces of the men who produce the money, especially the women who look as tightly wound up as Humphrey Bogart on the screen, and these *luftmenshen* who live on air, are air themselves. No books. No decent pictures. Not even good reproductions. No art. You seldom hear music. They lead a good second-rate existence. If I had their money. . .

Almost everybody is eager to answer the questions. To help all they can. The interviews are usually swift, to the point. Only with the unmarried women past thirty is there a touch of sadness, an intrusion. When you ask, were you ever married, the women, inevitably, in a tone of real regret, say, no, I've never been married. And you look around, at their attempts to turn a one-room apartment into a home, living among strangers, hard streets, and you feel sad, and look down on your form to save them the embarrassment of looking into your eyes.

There are people proud to tell you that they have a television set. Artists insulted, pride injured, egos squirming, when you innocently ask: how many hours did you work last week? And painters who straightway answer the questions. Executives who refuse to commit themselves to work hours; executives who answer a simple question simply. Women who lie miserably about their age; women who don't give a damn. One-time immigrants who've been in America for thirty years, ashamed to say they're not citizens. People who live in slums, apologetic when they say they have no bathtub, no toilet, no heat, instead of saying like one old Jewish woman: "Why do you ask me that? This is a slum. A dirty slum. A place to live. It's a slum. Write that down. A slum."

There are all kinds of people, of course, but wherever you go, one sentiment is so strong in all of the people that you begin to realize it comes from something basic and deep in the American character, rather than a fleeting manifestation invoked by the census. At first, superficially, it seems to come from the urge "to be counted." Nobody wants to be left out. Everybody wants to be included in the big count. But the welcome, the readiness to invite you in, the offer of drinks, cigarettes, even dinner, the best chair, a desk—all this is their way of showing the government in Washington, D. C., that it still belongs to the people, and they can afford to be generous when it makes an extraordinary request. The pattern was repeated over and over again. Only once was there any fear expressed that the census might be used as a way of obtaining damaging information. Which is not to say that the people are unaware of dangerous possibilities in current politics, but rather to say that they are conscious of their own strength. A strength that has been observed and recorded by too many people to bear much repetition here. But there it was. A genuine concern to be included in the big count, to help make up the total American picture, hospitality, warmth, even to the extent of tuning the sound out on the television set until the end of the interview.

The Conspirators

THE THREE PEOPLE, THE YOUNG MAN, HIS WIFE, AND
Mrs. Grady, hurried along the empty dark street talking about God,
his blessing and power. They had only met an hour ago through the
mutual introduction of Mrs. Mitchell in her flat on Christopher
Street, but already they had established that curious bond that makes
it possible for people to speak openly and honestly to one another.

"I get some holy water from the Father to put in the cupboard.
What do you do?"

He didn't know what "he did." A hazy forced remembrance
swept over him of friends and relatives and old neighbors invited to
the new house, of people surging through inspecting all the rooms,
a great deal of drinking, big open corned beef sandwiches, salami,
pickles, cake, bread his mother had baked, cases of pop and beer
cooling off in the bathtub, loud talk and dancing. "We have parties,"
he told Mrs. Grady, "and the people all bring us gifts for the new
house, stuff themselves with food, and get a little drunk." Mrs.
Grady laughed, but that wasn't a real answer for her.

"Don't you do anything for good luck?"

He remembered that his mother used to put salt, no, not salt but a
piece of bread in the cupboard. That was the custom brought over
from Russia, to put a piece of bread in the cupboard, the first piece
of bread to enter the new house. And that piece of bread was to

26

protect you and make your home a blessing for all the days of your life. And for Mrs. Grady there was a little holy water stored up in a bottle on the top shelf.

"Your God tells you to use bread. My God tells me to use holy water. Ain't it a crazy world? But I'll tell you something, kids, you can't always trust God. I know. That's why I want to help you kids out. We've got to help each other, don't we?"

He didn't know what to say in answer to Mrs. Grady. It's seldom that one finds oneself talking about God as though he existed in the flesh and watched over us like a kind father. He thought for a minute of all the arguments about the existence of God he had listened to during four years of college. Now that school was over for him and he was faced with the more serious problem of finding an apartment and putting to use his knowledge, he seldom had occasion to talk about God. He felt for a minute like really extending the argument with Mrs. Grady. Why does God tell you to use holy water, why does he tell me to use bread? But he knew that he couldn't reach the face-to-face depth of Mrs. Grady in an argument about God. God just wasn't a fundamental issue for him.

Mrs. Grady wouldn't have understood for a minute what was going on in the young man's head but she did know that tonight she was out on an adventure and the excitement of the idea aroused her. It was really possible to feel yourself alive, reaching to help other people, to collect events all around you. And you could do all of this without getting drunk. All gin could do was to make you drunk enough so that you could stand in the hallway of your tenement building and scream at the top of your voice for your dead husband Harry to come back from the grave and take care of you and sleep with you and give you little girls who could walk straight. The gin could make you forget the two little girls who had died and the five kids who remained alive after Harry was laid away in the ground in a soldier's pauper grave. But the gin couldn't make you feel alive. Mrs. Grady knew that she had to sum up her feelings.

"I'm going to help you kids because I know that you need help. Mrs. Mitchell told me all about the rat hole you're living in now. It ain't fit for kids like you. You need help. You're Jewish. I'm Irish.

So what? We all need help, don't we? And I don't want you to think that you have to pay me for the place. I won't take a penny. I'm telling you right now, I won't take a penny."

He listened in amazement. It just wasn't real. Weren't all the cheap bastards getting $200 to $300 for cold-water flats and didn't you have to pay off the supers or else buy a houseful of furniture that wasn't worth a dime? He looked at his wife and she gave him the look he expected. She couldn't believe it either. She was thinking of the kitchen. The place they were headed for had a kitchen. A large kitchen, Mrs. Grady had said. And there was a stove in the kitchen that had three burners and an oven. She could cook! The talk about God had slipped past her. She only knew that there was a possibility that before the night was over they might have a three-room apartment with a kitchen where she could cook and store utensils and do all of the things she couldn't do since her marriage.

The west wind from the Hudson River quickened their pace. They were approaching the big tenement buildings that had been thrown up around the turn of the century to house Irish workers who had given up their homes in Ireland to spend their days in cold, dark, crowded flats.

"That's the building over there," Mrs. Grady said. "Nobody's awake at this hour. They only stay up late on Friday nights. If you move in at one o'clock in the morning everything will be all right. Frankie and some of his friends moved me out at two in the morning. Nobody saw us and nobody heard us. The super still thinks I'm living in the flat. You've got nothing to worry about, kids, you'll come out all right. If anybody says anything to you, you can say you're my niece and nephew. Can't I have a Jewish nephew?"

If you move in at one in the morning. He tried to think out what the phrase meant. But he couldn't. They still had to see the rooms. To walk up the stairs. To test the toilet. To see the light connections. To look for the cockroaches. To worry about painting. And light. And air.

They stopped in front of the building. Mrs. Grady showed her nervousness. If she were caught in the empty flat the super might complain to the renting agent that she had vacated it and they would throw a padlock on the door.

"There's nothing to be afraid of, kids," she said, "just walk up the stairs like you're visiting a couple of friends."

The hallway was long and dark. The stairs were wooden. They mounted the stairs and began the long climb to the fifth floor.

"The only good thing about living up so high is the roof in the summertime. And you don't get any noise. It's nice in the summertime," Mrs. Grady explained. These were the steps she had climbed up and down for seventeen years. Her own mother had lived on the third floor until the day she died. She had climbed these stairs seven times pregnant. Twice she had held a wake. Oh, the stories she could tell.

The young wife withdrew into herself. Maybe having a kitchen wasn't such a wonderful idea after all. They could go on living in a furnished room until the housing situation let up. People were always finding apartments. They could cut corners a little and pay a little more rent. They could put off having a baby. They could try a little harder to find a place to live. Her husband was a veteran. Veterans had a certain kind of preference. They could find a place out of the city. The subways traveled fast. It didn't make any difference where they lived. Didn't other people find places to live? Didn't they find rooms open and aboveboard so that they could hire a moving van, sweep out their rooms, wash the windows, hang up curtains without being afraid? . . .

He saw immediately that the place was a firetrap. The hallways stunk of flooded toilets. If there was a God, he wanted to say to Mrs. Grady, would he permit us to sneak into our own home like a couple of thieves? He didn't say it because he knew how crazy it would sound. Why talk about God? Wasn't this a problem for people who wanted to change the face of the earth? Mrs. Grady brought him back to reality.

"This is the apartment, kids, let's go in."

The door opened into the kitchen. The room was bare except for the stove. The sudden light startled the roaches.

"You've got to see the place with furniture in mind," Mrs. Grady tried to explain. "It doesn't look like anything this way." But she knew they were disappointed. She felt that she would have been disappointed herself if she had been twenty years younger and looking at the first available apartment that had come up in over two years. It was a shameful place to live. And especially for a nice young couple. They would have no bathtub and would have to share a toilet in the hallway. And she looked like such a clean young girl— somebody used to taking a shower every morning and brushing her teeth in a white bathroom.

But what could she do? The place was vacant and she was willing to give it to them. And they wouldn't have to pay a penny for the apartment. It was still her apartment and she could do anything that she wanted with it. Didn't she pay rent on it for over seventeen years? What could people do? You've got to make your own bed. They were young kids. They could fix up the place. Maybe they could find a better place to live in after awhile. The rent was cheap, they could cook, and it was better than living in a lousy little furnished room. They could make the place look like something. And didn't Frankie just finish painting the place a nice sea-green? And wasn't the kitchen painted a new white? She and Harry had lived here. They had had seven kids. What difference does it make where you live?

The husband and wife looked at one another. How could they move in? How could they get the heart to sneak in their belongings at one o'clock in the morning.

"You've got nothing to worry about, kids," Mrs. Grady told them. "Everybody is doing it. How do you think people like us get apartments? We've got to help each other. If I had just let the place go, the renting agent would be getting $60.00 a month for this hole. And then where would you be? I tell you that everybody in this house is living under somebody else's name. It's the only way we can live now with high rents and no place to move to."

She was right. They both knew it. There was no place else to go. That was reality.

"Your friends will help. Just like my friends helped me sneak-move into my new place. We've got to keep helping each other."

Mrs. Grady knew they would take the place and she was happy. People who needed help were taking over the flat. It wouldn't go to the landlord. For the past eight days she had been frantic lest the apartment slip out of her hands when the rent came due. It wasn't the apartment so much as getting back at the landlord. Didn't he tell her to get out in the street with her little girl who was just out of the hospital, if she didn't like living in three rooms. Didn't the doctor warn her that her little girl would crack up again unless she found an apartment with steam heat, a bathtub, and a private toilet. Didn't she bury two little girls already. Didn't she bury Harry in a soldiers' pauper grave. Didn't the landlord give a four-room apartment that had become vacant to somebody who could spend $60.00 a month while she walked the streets half-crazy trying to find a bigger place to live. Oh if Harry could have only been alive tonight to see the way she acted.

Her dead soldier husband would have been proud of her.

The Visitor

"THERE'S MA!" NAOMI POINTED. DAN LOOKED DOWN through the open gates of the train entrance into the gloom of the tracks. Naomi's mother came alone, wearing a gray Persian lamb coat, carrying no baggage. Her face broke into a smile of recognition as she saw Naomi waving, and then she ran forward to kiss Naomi and press her lips on Dan. Wet, no warmth, though she pressed her mouth against his with a firm touch. He looked at her face as she kissed Naomi again. No change from the first time he had seen her, though now her skin was whiter, her lips thinner, her eyes sunken. He didn't like the side of her face, the taut muscles that gave way to a quivering, drawing her lips thin. She had no complaints. But complain she did. And he remembered that when no one listened to her complaints she contorted her body, dragged her legs, stretched her features across the bony skeleton of her face and cried, Look! Dan thought he knew her whole history. He and Naomi had been over it a dozen times, particularly in the last month, waiting for her mother to come. And each time they talked Naomi revealed a bit more and he hoped that one day she would reveal enough to free herself from her useless antagonism and see her mother for what she was, a woman with an absolutely unique relation to her.

"Let's take a cab," Dan suggested.

"Won't it be expensive?" Naomi's mother asked.

"Not much more than taking a subway and then a taxi to the house. We don't live very far in Brooklyn. Just across the bridge."

The redcap came up with her luggage and wheeled the bags across the concourse to the taxi station. In a moment they were out of the station and in the midst of the 42nd Street traffic.

"New York City . . ." Naomi's mother said. "You can tell it by the noise." Naomi's mother stretched her neck out of the taxi window for a minute and then she settled back in the seat. "You showed it all to me the last time, remember the things we saw, Dan, that you wrote down on a piece of paper?" He had shown his in-laws the city. The ice skaters at Radio City, Sak's Fifth Avenue— and the rotted wooden steps leading up four flights to the cold flat on Jane Street he and Naomi had then, three small rooms, no bath-room, two toilet bowls for four families. And Naomi's mother sat down on the studio bed almost hysterical from the long climb, the smells in the hallway. "The people across the street pay $165 for three rooms," he tried to tell her. And Naomi tried to say, "Ma, you don't understand New York." And Naomi's mother said, "All I know is that you live in a dump, a dirty dump! And I wouldn't live here for the world!" The argument didn't end but it was forgotten rushing in and out of subways.

The taxi crossed the Manhattan Bridge and before Dan could point out the downtown skyline, the East River emptying into the Bay, the cab turned into Brooklyn. Manhattan lay on the other side of the bridge. Brooklyn? It was like every other city he had seen, only larger, more like the sadness of an enormous rooming house. Dan didn't consider himself a native. He and Naomi had only moved to Brooklyn because of a vacant apartment on the Heights. He knew Naomi's mother would like their apartment. Didn't Naomi spend two weeks washing the woodwork, the toilet, waxing the floors, cleaning their two rooms as thoroughly as he remembered scrubbing down the barracks for a general inspection. He screamed, "Don't imitate your mother!" And Naomi screamed back, "I'm not!" And he remembered thinking: examine the mother before you marry. But before they closed the door to take the IRT to Grand Central the apartment looked like a show window on 57th Street.

"This is Brooklyn," Dan announced. The taxi turned away from the factory buildings on the water front, the red-brick tenements Naomi's mother must have remembered from Jane Street, and crossed into Henry Street, riding down the lane of modern apartments, the turn-of-the-century mansions.

"This is nice," Naomi's mother said.

"It's even nicer on the water." The taxi turned into Montague Street. Dan and Naomi looked at one another as they passed the towering modern building on the corner. "This way, driver." The cab stopped and Dan paid the fare, ignoring the outstretched money in his mother-in-law's hand. He took her two bags and led the way up the brownstone steps that rose to the entrance of their building. The lamp in the hallway lit the old polished black-walnut paneling. The mirror in the hallway rose twenty feet to the ceiling. And in the big mirror Naomi's mother pointed to her own image. The whiteness of her skin was softened by the yellow parchment lamp. "I came for a rest," she announced, "no running around. No subway riding. I want you to do me a favor, Dan. Please see to it that I drink a quart of milk a day and that I get plenty of rest. I don't even want to go to the radio shows."

"You'll get your first rest now. There's only one flight of stairs to climb."

The stairway was wide and grand, the railing made of black walnut and at the top of the stairs Dan pointed to the door that opened into their apartment. "We have this half of this half of the floor."

"It's different—"

"Than Jane Street," Naomi interrupted her mother.

"Let's go in." Dan opened the big door that once led to the second-floor master library and stepped aside to let Naomi's mother enter first.

"It's beautiful!" And it was beautiful! A beam of north light flooded the room. The rug was spotless. The furniture waxed and shining. The colors of their books lit one whole wall. The paintings hung, filling the space of the fifteen foot ceiling. And scattered around the room were the pieces they had picked up at auction, cherry tables, stuffed Victorian chairs, the studio couch covered in red corduroy that Naomi's mother would sleep on.

"The rent is cheap, Ma, and we got the place by a miracle."

"Believe me, I wouldn't ever move back to Manhattan if I were you. Not that dump—" And she quickly added, turning to Dan, "you know what I mean, Dan. It *was* a dump. This is something nice."

Dan didn't answer but took her luggage into the small adjoining room that served as a bedroom. "I'll get along with the kids," she probably said, over and over again, on the train, at home in her kitchen, in bed. "I'm going for a rest. No quarrels. No fights." She had to declare peace. Because there had been no peace in the past. Not once. Not when he married Naomi. Not on their visits home to Detroit. She didn't like his haircut, his socks, clothes, shirts, his whole life, his writing, the dribble of money that came in, least of all his marrying Naomi. And now she was going to live with him and Naomi for at least two weeks and she would see how Naomi went off to work while he stayed at home and lay around on the studio couch, played records, tried to sit at his typing desk, typed a little, and then about five o'clock began to prepare supper, peeling potatoes, shopping for meat, setting the table. But she had seen stranger things herself. The swift passage of time. And now she was fifty-seven and holding on to a thread. And how she must sway with the thread, unable to retreat like a spider.

Naomi was making coffee when Dan came back into the living room. "How do you like the place now that you've sat in it?" he asked.

"I was telling Naomi that I can't get over it. And the rent is only $23.00 more than what you were paying in that other place."

"A friend told us about it. That's the only way you can find an apartment. Unless you're lucky."

"Luck—" she said, "and money."

Naomi came in with three cups of coffee and a tray of hot toast. "No milk?" Dan asked. And Naomi's mother laughed. "He wants to make me fat in a hurry!"

The afternoon passed quickly. At five o'clock Dan went out

shopping. He bought two pounds of lamb chops. He remembered the last time he had made Swiss steak in the pressure cooker. Naomi's mother wouldn't touch the food. He picked up some creamed filet of herring for an appetizer and a long loaf of French bread.

"I love French bread!" was the first thing Naomi's mother said when he emptied his packages. "The doctor says that I can't eat it but I do anyway."

"Did the doctor tell you why you can't eat French bread?" Dan asked.

"No," was all the answer Dan got. And it occurred to him that her doctor probably picked out white bread, raisins and green peppers, labeled them injurious. What could the doctor do? He was a doctor, not a metaphysician. Pains came. Backaches, cramps, headaches. "But I eat French bread whenever we go out to a restaurant," she added. And that was the way she had lived her life. The world was the white bread she couldn't eat. And no doctor could tell her why she couldn't eat the white bread. But she broke the crust and nibbled enough to know the world was inside of her—Dan smiled when he saw her break the end of the hard crust.

"I want to put on twelve pounds," she said to Dan.

"Milk, water and bread will do it."

"He wants to starve me to death!" she said, laughing, and they all laughed.

Naomi made up her mother's bed at one o'clock. The time from dinner to bed passed quickly. Only once did an argument begin. But her mother quickly made peace. "Naomi, honey, it's nothing to argue about." And it wasn't anything to argue about. The price of furniture. Their apartment was filled with auction pieces, a second-hand desk, even a captain's chair they had picked up on the sidewalk, but Naomi had to defend her knowledge of the prices of custom furniture. And she shouted, "You can't buy a wing chair for under $500." "Naomi, honey, you can buy a beautiful wing chair for a $100, maybe a little less or more." "Mother, I know the price of good furniture. We have friends who—" "I'm not saying you can't spend more, honey. I mean that you can buy a good chair for a little less money." Dan thought he knew what his mother-in-law was trying to say. He had seen the way she studied their old, faded, Victorian chair. She must have been thinking of a gift to buy for the house. Her mother did like to buy presents; perhaps it was a peace offering she made to people. He didn't know. The price of a good wing chair wasn't resolved, but the argument seemed to lift a load of uneasiness from Naomi.

"It's time for sleep," Dan announced at one o'clock.

"Sleep—" Naomi's mother said.

"Didn't you sleep on the train?" Dan asked.

"I was afraid to take a sleeping pill with all of the money I was carrying."

"Do you take sleeping pills?"

"The doctor advised them. I have a terrible time going to sleep at night."

"But they're no good for you."

"I know. I know. But what else can I do to fall asleep? You don't know how terrible it is to lie in bed and not be able to sleep. Not for a whole year. Just once to lie down and sleep . . ." The word "sleep" ended in a moan.

"You'll be able to sleep in this bed," Dan could only say, pointing to the studio couch.

"I hope so."

"How many pillows do you want, mother?" Naomi asked.

"Just one, dear."

Naomi fluffed the pillow and turned back the white sheet. Her mother went into the kitchen and came back with a glass of water. "For the pill," she said to Dan, "I hope I won't have to take any more after this." She swallowed the pill and they said goodnight.

In the dark bedroom Naomi asked Dan what he thought. He merely grumbled an answer. They were both conscious of the rustling of the sheets. Only a thin wall separated the two rooms. The studio couch and the bed lay alongside one another. He could feel Naomi start each time the sheets made a sound. No sound came from the living room. Each rustle of their sheet sounded as though a mad orgy was going on and to end the nonsense Dan took Naomi in his arms.

Naomi made breakfast in the morning. Orange juice, fried eggs, bacon, heated rolls, and she laid out the silver they seldom used. Dan always marveled that people found words to say to one another after getting up in the morning. Naomi's mother was full of talk, mostly about sleep. The studio bed she made up the instant after wakening, smoothing the corduroy cover into place. "It's a bed that I can sleep on," she told Dan. And Dan was learning to translate her statements: she wasn't satisfied with her bed at home though her bed at home was brand-new with layers of cotton felt and horsehair.

Naomi and Dan insisted on doing the breakfast dishes alone. Naomi's mother sat in the old walnut captain's chair they had picked up on the street, and looked out of the bay window. "Where does the fog go to?" she called to Dan in the kitchenette. "What—" he called back. "The fog," she said, "you can see it just going away." "The hot and cold air balance one another," Dan said, not sure of his explanation, "and when there's a balance the sky becomes clear again." "Oh—" was all she said. She looked out of the window toward the Bay. The late morning sky was performing its magic. The eye had no chance to rest. It picked up the tops of the freighters. The stubby stacks of tugboats. The lazy pattern of the ferryboats. And the city. Still a dim gray outline of towers pushing through the mist. Her body in the old walnut chair didn't edge forward but settled back in the graceful curve of the bent wood. She looked middle-aged, gentle. For the first time in months she hadn't spent all morning scrubbing down the kitchen stove, carpet-sweeping a rug that took more punishment than cleaning, ending exhausted in a telephone chair, not knowing why her hand shook when she dialed the phone or from what part of her body there rose a thumping emptiness that seemed to flatten her out until her voice cried louder and louder into the telephone making plans for a poker game.

Dan came in from the kitchenette with a full glass of orange juice. "More juice to make you fat," he said, offering her the glass.

Naomi's mother laughed again. "I've just finished eating."

"I'm thinking of the Promenade. The orange juice will ward off any colds when you sit on the bench."

"Let's go out now for a walk," Naomi suggested from the kitchenette. "The dishes are all done."

Naomi, her mother and Dan turned from Columbia Heights into the Promenade.

"The air smells clean!" Naomi's mother said.

"That's from the Atlantic Ocean," Dan told her.

"Is this the Atlantic Ocean?"

"No, this is only the Bay. But there," and his arm made a sweep around the Bay, past Erie Basin into the Narrows, "around this tip of Brooklyn is the whole Atlantic Ocean."

"How did such a thing ever come together?" she asked Dan.

"The whole world is practically water," Dan explained.

"Not the whole world?"

"And people are almost all water."

"Sometimes I wish we were."

The air was damp and it left the benches wet. They walked along the bare, deserted stretch of the Promenade and Dan pointed out their bay window, the mansions that lay behind the long, extended, green iron fence. "Once," Dan said, "a single family had all of one of these houses. Horse carriages drove up and down Columbia Heights."

"People come and go," Naomi's mother said. And she said it on a voice so that you knew the dead were dead and the living alive. A boarded-up cross-piece ended the Promenade. Beyond lay an unfinished stretch that would be opened soon. Dan turned up Clark Street and led Naomi's mother into Willow Street. He thought she might enjoy the sight of the old Dutch houses but instead she complained of the dampness in the air and they turned from the quiet little street into Columbia Heights.

Dan didn't know how the afternoon would end. Naomi had gone off to her job and he felt strange at his desk, as though he was supposed to produce work. He had no work planned. His mind had come to a halt when he heard Naomi's mother was on her way to New York. He knew it would be impossible to work with her in the house. It was difficult enough to work alone. He sat with his back to

Naomi's mother for about fifteen minutes and then he turned from his chair to see that she had dozed off. The fresh air and long walk stretched her out along a corner of the studio couch. Her legs were drawn stiff as though she knew in her sleep she wasn't supposed to dirty the studio couch. Is she dreaming now? And he wondered if the faces of people changed as they dreamt. If you could read a dream as you read fear, confusion, diffidence. Probably not. Dreams were below the surface of the face. He thought of slipping off her shoes, but that would probably wake her. He let her sleep and then turned back in his chair. The sun gave up its battle with the clouds. The room lay dark. A dim gray light reflected some of the keys on his typewriter. He ran his hands over the helpless keys and slipped down in his chair closing his eyes.

"It's dark!" And when Dan turned around, Naomi's mother added, "You've been sleeping too!" And they both laughed like lovers. Dan turned on the lamp by the bay window. He stretched his arms to show that he had really been sleeping. His sleep had been soundless. "I don't remember when the last time was that I dozed off like this," Naomi's mother said, "I'm afraid to doze in the afternoon—then I can't fall asleep at night."

"Dozing puts weight on you. If you slept an hour after lunch and supper you'd put on all the weight you wanted."

"No Dan, I'm afraid for my sleep. A person has to sleep." Once or twice he had been unable to really fall asleep and he had a glimpse into that tossing world of twisting from side to side, digging your head into the pillow, trying to remember what sleep was like.

Dan began supper and she insisted on peeling the potatoes. And he finally let her prepare the chopped round steak the way she liked best. "Naomi always loved it this way." She worked with short quick steps in the kitchenette. The chopped meat was rolled into patties and the salad made up when Naomi rang the door buzzer. Dinner lasted until ten o'clock. And after washing the dishes they talked until two o'clock. Dan swore he didn't know the source of all the words. But then a simple question opened a flood. "Didn't you once win a dancing cup, Ma," Naomi asked. And her mother retold the history of her life. Dan leaned forward, anxious to hear the story

from her own lips, but as she spoke, he realized her story was no
different from the stories Naomi had told him. The history of her
life, then, was a well-remembered anecdote. He didn't expect a full
confession. Or maybe he did. She seemed to be ten thousand miles
away from home. In two days he had noticed a change, and he
wondered what would happen after ten days. But people aren't
chameleons. And he was happy she didn't take a sleeping pill when
they finally all went to bed.

Naomi took her mother shopping in the morning. And when
they came home at four in the afternoon, Dan knew there had been
trouble. He felt they both had had to get a quarrel out of their
systems, and the quarrel had probably exploded while shopping. It
had. In the eighth-floor lamp department at Macy's. "I won't go
shopping again," Naomi's mother told Dan. "That girl, she doesn't
know what she wants." "Mother, I told you I didn't like the lamps at
Macy's." "No, she'd rather buy an old, dirty lamp at an auction
sale." "An old, dirty lamp isn't always a piece of junk! You've been
saying our furniture is junk ever since you came here." "Naomi,
honey, I didn't. I merely said if you get some money you'll be able
to buy nicer things. I like your table and chair, I think they're beautiful, but don't tell me that my daughter thinks this is the best furniture
that money can buy." "I don't put a price tag on my furniture!"
"Honey, I'm not saying that you do, but other people do." The
argument had shaken Naomi's mother, left her face drawn, and when
she got up to walk she contorted her back, placing her hand on
her hip, limping over to the studio couch. Naomi and Dan both
looked at one another at the same instant. The agony was false.
And it made them helpless not to be able to shout, Ma! straighten
out your back! They watched her fluff a pillow on the studio couch
and carefully place it against her back, easing herself on the couch
with a soft moan.

"Why don't we have some ice cream?" Naomi suggested.

"None for me," Naomi's mother said in a hurt voice.

"They make wonderful Syrian ice cream on Atlantic Avenue,"
Dan said flatly, and he put on his coat and went out for a pint of
ice cream.

Naomi left for work early the next morning. Dan and Naomi's mother did the breakfast dishes. No mention was made of the quarrel. They washed and wiped the dishes between them, cleaning up the small dining area in the living room.

"It's crazy the way I clean house at home. But it's funny, Dan, when you have your own house you like it to be neat."

"Everybody likes to be neat," Dan said, "but that doesn't mean cleaning day and night."

"I won't from now on, Dan. You've seen what cleaning house has done to me. My back won't stop aching. I thought I'd scream in my sleep last night."

"You should take more holidays."

"I will," she laughed.

"To Florida, California, the sun will warm your back."

"It takes money, Dan."

"Money—" was all Dan said.

"You and Naomi don't care about money, do you, Dan?"

"That's not so," Dan said. "I'm sick and tired of people telling us that we don't care about money. You have to care about money. It takes money to live. To get on the subway. Buy a newspaper. Make a phone call."

"But what I mean, Dan, is that you don't like to make money the way other people make money. I wish I could be like you, Dan. You think about yourself, that's good."

"Don't you think about yourself?"

"I wish I could. I wouldn't care about money if I could sleep. Here I can sleep. But at home . . . A person can get through a day. But the night . . . It's thinking all the time about other people, the house, the furniture, cleaning the carpet. I can't stop myself from getting up in the morning and scrubbing down the stove. You know what goes on at home, Dan. When I think back to the way I used to torture myself—" and she turned pleading to Dan. "Dan, you're smart. What happens to a person so that they quit thinking about themself? To live like a stranger to your own life. How . . ?" Dan didn't know what to say. He was too surprised to hear her say that she knew she swayed on a thread. He didn't want to snap the motion. Nor could he set her life in order. That was magic. So he kept silent. And she went on to say, "But what can you do when the past is over?" The urgency left her voice. Dan held the dustpan while she swept up the crumbs from the floor. "Look, Dan," she said, "the floor's done and it didn't take a minute."

Dan didn't even want to go through the pretense of sitting at his desk, so he suggested they take a walk to Fulton Street. "It's the big shopping center of Brooklyn," he explained, "all of the Fifth Avenue shops have stores there."

"We can look at the lamps again. I want to buy you and Naomi a present for the house."

They dressed warm against the wind that swept up from the Bay. The sun was out but it was a cold, white winter day. Dan took her up Pierrepont Street past the impressive mansions and found himself quoting the high rentals of the apartments. "Maybe some day you'll be able to afford a nicer apartment," she said. Dan caught the tone of her voice and he was sorry they had started out of the apartment. But he had no reason for turning back now. The apartment isolated her. But Fulton Street. It was like the world she lived in. "Look at the people!" she cried, "I thought Brooklyn was nothing. And look at the shops! There's no reason to go into Manhattan."

Dan took her into Abraham & Straus's and they rode the elevator from "ladies clothes" to "shoes," finally to the sixth floor, where a whole vast floor of modern furniture came into view as they left the elevator.

"Don't tell me this isn't good stuff!" The floor of furniture was the world she lived in. "And if you and Naomi had the money you'd buy this instead of auction pieces."

"Sure," Dan said, "in a minute."

"What's wrong with this furniture? Don't tell me the people who buy it aren't as good as you and Naomi."

"There's nothing wrong with this furniture, nothing at all."

"And if you had the money you'd buy it." Dan could feel an argument coming on. It was wrong to take her shopping. It brought her too close to the gray world covered with glory that she wanted him and Naomi to enter. "Look at this wing chair," she drove on, "now don't tell me your chair in the living room is as good as this."

"What do you want me to say!" he finally had to tell her, "that this chair is better than our chair! I don't give a damn about either chair. The way you live is the way you buy furniture."

"Dan, honey, I'm not saying anything about you and Naomi. I'm just saying that there is good furniture that you can buy if you have the money."

Dan let the apology stand. He didn't believe in miracles. And when she put her hand on her hip and began to limp he knew it was time to go back. "Shopping tires you out like nothing else," she said, explaining her limp. Dan picked up a cab on Fulton Street. The wind blew from the west and it would be punishment to try and walk down Montague Street. He said nothing on the ride. The wind almost blew them over when they stepped out on Columbia Heights.

"A cup of hot tea," Naomi's mother suggested. She filled the tea kettle and took down the chocolate cookies she had bought. Dan sat in his chair and stabbed at the typewriter keys.

"Working, Dan?" she called from the kitchenette.

"No."

He got up from the chair and put a record on, Beethoven's *Fourth Piano Concerto*. The whitecaps out on the Bay made him think of Beethoven. He liked his record player, the rich, true tone that came like magic out of the pine box he had hammered together. The parts he had bought on Cortlandt Street. "What's that?" Naomi's mother asked. "Beethoven." "It's beautiful." He had played several records the first day she came but the pine box closed her ears. She probably didn't think music could come out of a corner speaker. But now she listened. Perhaps it was the wind outside. The wind made you listen. You wondered how it came out of the cold white sky and where the sound went when it left your ears. Why should there be wind? And why should wind have a sound? Or maybe it was her limp. Or his anger. Or the silent cab ride. Naomi's mother poured two cups of steaming tea. "Don't you have to change the record?" she asked.

"No," Dan said, "it plays that way for at least half an hour." The piano cadenza came on. And you knew that a man was hitting the keys making all the beautiful sounds. "How does a man learn to do that?" Naomi's mother asked. Dan shook his head. "People," she said. "Tell me, Dan" she asked, "how is it possible that there are so many different people in the world? No two people look alike. Every face different." He shook his head again. "And for one man to learn to play like that." Dan sipped on his tea. The gray white light coming from the bay window softened his mother-in-law's face. The still, quiet Beethoven music with its points of infinite reaching from one idea to another and then just losing out in a new swelling theme, seemed to reach her. She didn't ask for any more explanations but merely listened, forgetting her tea, and when he rose to change the side she didn't break the stillness. "It's beautiful," she repeated when the record came to an end. Dan put on the Brahms Concerto. The two concertos filled almost all the afternoon. The sun was past Jersey when Dan put on Mahler's *The Song of the Earth*. "Oh," was all she said. But he thought she would weep or cry or step out of her chalk-white skin.

On the next afternoon Naomi's mother asked Dan to play the Mahler again. She sat in the captain's chair and listened, turning her chair so that it faced the speaker and the Bay. And when Dan got up to turn the record, she said, "I have to go home sometime. I can't stay here forever."

"You've only been away a few days."

"And my Maury's been eating in restaurants. What day do you think I should go home, Dan?"

"I don't know." He didn't want to mention a definite date. Then he knew she would feel unwelcome. "Tuesday or Wednesday is a good time to travel. The trains aren't crowded."

"The house—it'll be a mess when I get home. Dust everywhere. The stove to wash. The bathroom. You see, Dan, you can't stop the way you said. The house has to be cleaned—" and then she paused and asked, "and if I stop cleaning the house?"

"The house isn't your whole life!"

"What is my life, Dan?"

"Look what you did here," was all that Dan could say. He didn't believe in magic. And he didn't like to be forced into telling lies.

"But this," and she pointed to the books, the Mahler record spinning on the turntable, "is your life, Naomi's, not mine."

"Then what is your life?" The words were out and they hung in the room like the dust that turns the sun into a red ball.

"My life—?" she asked, and she looked at Dan, her eyes swallowing him up. "You know, Dan. You know."

Naomi's mother decided to leave on Wednesday. "Thursday morning I'll be home. Will you be glad?" she asked Dan and Naomi at supper.

"No," Dan said flatly.

"We had our fights," she said. "Over the lamp. The chair."

"Oh, mother," Naomi said, "all families fight."

"I wonder," she asked Dan, "if there's a reason for it."

The IRT express train carried them straight to Grand Central Station Wednesday afternoon. Dan checked the luggage through and then they all walked out of the station to 42nd Street.

"This is New York again," Naomi's mother said.

"Look, there's the second tallest building in the world." Naomi's mother lifted her face toward the Chrysler Building. In the harsh sunlight Dan could see just a bit of color in her chalk whiteness. But a lot of the tightness had left her face. And why not? Only one sleeping pill. He wondered if she would listen to the records again, look into the lament that made her cry "Oh." Why should she? Except that she had asked him on the subway down to Grand Central, "Dan, do they ever play that piece on television?"

Only a small cluster of people waited at the train gate when they returned from a snack at Hector's in Times Square. Dan bought two tuna fish sandwiches and had them wrapped to take out. "They're going to Detroit," Naomi's mother told the counterman and they all laughed. A guard in a blue uniform opened the iron gate and people began filing through.

"There'll be plenty of seats."

Naomi started to kiss her mother but then her mother took hold of Naomi and kissed Naomi full on her lips. Dan saw her face start when she looked past Naomi down the long gloomy tunnel leading to the train coaches. He started to reach forward to kiss her good-bye when she surprised him by taking him around like a lover and kissing him warm on his lips, her mouth pressing against his as warm and fresh and biting into his lips as a trembling girl.

Just Love, Love, Sweet Love

HE MOANED LOUDER THAN THE PAIN BEGRIEVED.

"Do something! Do something! Stop the pain! Cut it out! Take off my leg! Don't take my leg! I don't want to lose my leg, save my leg, don't take my leg, my beautiful leg, I need my leg, don't take my leg!"

The interne on emergency duty didn't dare give the moaning man a sedative to quiet him. The narcotic might kill him. He had to be on duty tonight. Only him. His luck. Why weren't these cases all shipped to Bellevue, that's where these moaning bastards belonged, they were all as good as dead already, walking stiffs, no good to anyone, so much garbage. How did they stay alive?

"Does he have to scream like that?" the anxious night nurse asked the interne.

"No, he doesn't have to scream. He's just drunk, imagining most of his pain."

"But isn't there glass in his foot?"

"There's glass, probably plenty more. His foot is rotten with pus. It's been festering for days."

"I don't want to lose my leg! Would you like to lose your leg? What would you do without a leg, doctor? Hobble, dobble, tobble, wobble, no, doctor, you hang on to your leg. Don't you read the

Bible, doctor? Apocrypha! A man with one leg isn't naked before God. I need my leg. I want to die with my leg."

"How do you know about the Apocrypha?"

"Take a look at my drawings, doc, you'll see. Take a look. Oooooo, give me a needle. Cut this pain. Take a look at my drawings . . ."

"What drawings?"

"He brought this paper bag with him," the nurse motioned to the doctor.

The interne reached for the brown paper grocery bag, opened it and took out a handful of white sheets covered with black-and-white pen-and-ink drawings.

"They're great!" the moaning man told the interne. "The greatest little drawings in the world. I'm the best black-and-white man since Daumier. The best in the whole damn world. There isn't anybody better than I am. Nobody under the blue heaven. Take a look. You'll get it. Pick one out, doc, put it in a little frame, hang it over your bed, it'll make you live, teach you new tricks, you're not too old to learn new tricks, my drawings will teach you new tricks."

The interne held one of the drawings under the lamp. The page was a smear of lines, swiftly drawn, caught up in a curious movement of their own. He handed one of the drawings over to the nurse. She smiled neatly at the interne. He smiled back.

"They're great, aren't they, doc. Look at them all, pick out the one you like. I'm the greatest painter of the century. That's why you've got to save my leg, doc, you've got to save my leg!"

"Look!" the interne shouted, losing control. "You're not going to lose your leg. You've got a piece of glass in your foot, some pus, but you're not going to lose your leg. Now I don't want to hear any more of your raving. We're just waiting for the head doctor to come down from the operating room. He'll say whether it's all right to give you a sedative so that we can work on your leg. Personally I think a shot of dope would kill you now with all that liquor in your system. And I don't like to say this but the place for you is Bellevue. They can really help you."

"No!" the patient said, alarmed, "you're not going to send me to

Bellevue. If I'm going to die I want to die here, brothers and sisters, in this hospital."

"Right now you aren't going anywhere, so just stay still."

The interne angrily left the emergency room and walked out into the corridor in search of the two men who had brought in the patient. He'd find out who this moaning idiot was, laughing, screaming, talking about God, pretending to be an artist. He found the two men sitting on a bench in the corridor heatedly talking to one another. Their voices dropped as they saw the interne.

"Tell me," the interne asked, leaning against the black-and-white tiled wall, the red emergency bulb darkening his soft white face, his body limp to suggest a kind of intrafraternity informality. "What sort of a person is this fellow you brought in?"

"What do you mean?" the shorter of the two men asked, pretending not to understand the question, disturbed by the obvious gesture of the interne.

"He claims that he's a painter—is he an artist?"

"Didn't he tell you that?" the friend of the artist replied, trying to keep his voice under control.

"I would just like to find out a bit more about him. He's in pretty bad shape. He rattles on and on, not at all like an artist—"

"He's a painter, we work together," the friend said tightly, warding off the implication of the interne.

"He's a painter, eh. Is he a good painter?" the interne asked.

"Yes, he's a good painter," the friend said, avoiding what he felt might be the beginning of an argument.

"Does he do it for a living? Does he make money at it?"

"Afraid he can't pay his bill, doc?"

The interne turned sharply and walked back into the emergency room. Who were these nuts dressed like bums, shoes covered with blotches of paint, shirts open when the wind was blowing outside. Stuyvesant Square was around the corner, Gramercy Park, Greenwich Village.

"There isn't anything you don't have to know, nurse, just learn to love people, love people, any kind of people, then you'll be a real nurse, that's love, any kind of people, take a man for what he is, that's all, just love, love is around the corner, you don't have to look for love, that's the big lie, everybody lies about love, nobody believes in love, just love, if you're a nurse you're going to have to love, you're not a nurse if you don't love, love, sweet love, love all the time. I once wrote a song about love, love is a diddle, love diddle day, the sky diddle day, love is diddle, diddle is love, love diddle day—"

"SHUT UP! I thought I told you to shut up!"

The artist stopped beating time to his song. The nurse turned to hide her red face.

"Do you always talk this way!" the interne still shouted, his voice hollow in the emergency room.

"A man only talks the way he can talk. I talk the way I feel. Now I feel love. This is love here. Sick people all of the floors above me, lying in the dark, knowing they're being attended to, just a doctor between them and dying. This is all love here—"

The interne didn't know what to say. He bent over and made a pretense of examining the painter's leg. "How does it feel?" he asked.

"Like hell!"

"I can't give you any kind of a shot until the head doctor says it's all right."

"Then I'll stay here for the night. In the morning you can give me a shot."

"There're only a couple of free beds. We've got to hold those for real emergency cases."

"My leg is a real emergency!"

"It's not an emergency the way we see an emergency!" the interne shouted. The man was dead drunk a minute ago, raving like a psycho. Now this face-to-face exchange. Nuts! The man was nuts. He should be committed to Bellevue. Painter! Those scribbled lines he looked at were another delusion. These damn artists thinking they could get their way with everything. Someday it'll all explode in their faces. What a colossal bunch of bull it was! Scribble a line, art—he'd break the back of the myth. Boom out of the window. Love is a diddle de doo. That was enough to send him away.

The white walls closed in on the painter. How long had he been

drinking? A week, a month, a year? Why didn't the pain stop?
That broken glass on his studio floor. Why did he bring his little
bag of drawings? He should have brought a big canvas with him,
the one hanging over the fireplace. That would make them jump.
The little line drawings weren't enough. No emergency! What was
an emergency? When did it begin? The exact moment before you
begin to die? He didn't want to die, he wanted to live in everybody's
world. What happened to the brains, the big hospitals, the medical
textbooks stacked higher than the clouds, white clouds, white coats,
stethoscope, boom, boom, boom, blood whirling, count the blood,
boom a beat on the stethoscope, what happened to this god man
mountain of knowledge, why couldn't they fix his leg after eight
thousand years, squeeze the pain out, send him back to his studio,
oh the stories he could tell now, a big canvas, eight feet by ten feet,
one white coat, the rest black, the white coat against the black, just
squeezed down, all the way down against the canvas, down to nothing, just nothing, wait for the head doctor, let's all wait for God
to come down and hold our hands and lead us through green fields,
just wait for God and he'll show us how to operate, dig out the pain,
dig out the glass, let the pus run clean, that's all, who was the head
doctor, which way is west, west is where the head doctor is coming
from, no more death, everybody lives, hurrah for the head doctor,
free pretzels, no more night, the head doctor is coming, nobody dies.

"Well, you're still now," the interne said to his patient. "Maybe
some of that alcohol is wearing off. If it does we might be able to
fix up your leg."

"That's all I want. I just want to be fixed up and go home."

"So you've got a home."

"Of course. You should come up to my studio and see my work."

"What kind of paintings do you turn out?"

"The best in the world."

"Does everybody think so?"

"Not everybody thinks."

"Nurse! prepare some hot water and a soap solution. We'll wash
his leg."

The interne didn't want to lose his temper again. He turned from the painter and rang the operating room. No answer. The head doctor must be on his way down.

The nurse began washing the patient's leg. "Let me do that, honey," he told her. "It's my dirty leg. Let me wash it. You keep those pretty hands for dying people. The dying need love because they're all alone. I'll wash my own dirty feet. There are only a couple of times in a man's life when it's important to have clean feet."

The head doctor walked in from surgery, still wearing his dirty white operating gown.

"So this is the man you phoned about." He bent over and took the artist's leg in his clean hand. His fingers traveled over the instep, up the calf, encircling the pus. He couldn't escape the heavy smell of whisky.

"How intoxicated is he?" the head doctor asked the interne, taking him aside.

"Too bad for an injection, I think."

"I'm inclined to think you're right. He'll have to sober up before we can do anything for him. Why didn't he go to Bellevue?"

"He said that he hates Bellevue, that if he has to die he wants to die here."

"Well, there's no room here tonight for him to die. How did he get here?"

"Two of his friends brought him in a cab."

"Are they still here?"

"They're waiting in the corridor."

"What do you know about him?" the head doctor asked, careful to keep his voice down.

"He's an artist of some sort from what I can gather. A little off his head. He's not a bum—"

"That's obvious from his face."

The artist looked at the whispering doctors.

"Well," the head doctor said to the emergency patient, "you're too intoxicated for us to do anything for you tonight."

"How can I sober up with all of this pain in my leg?"

"That's not the problem. The problem for you is to stay away from whisky. We can't stop the pain in your leg as long as you have whisky flooding up your system. It's too dangerous. You have a choice of staying here or else going home and returning in the morning. We won't turn you out."

The patient stood up, his foot still wet from the washing. The nurse handed him a towel.

"I'm going home," he said in a low tone.

"All right, it's still a free country," the head doctor said and then turned and left the room.

The patient put on his shoe, hobbled over to the desk to get his bag of drawings.

"I want you to soak that foot," the interne said officiously, leaning back in his chair, his hands folded together. "I want you to soak that foot and come back sober in the morning. Then we'll be able to do something for you. The only reason I'm permitting you to check out is because I think you have something on the ball."

"You're a nice boy, doctor, you're a nice boy. Good-bye, little boy blue," the emergency patient said gently and then with the help of his two friends he hobbled out of the room holding his paper bag of drawings.

The City

THE LEXINGTON AVENUE IRT EXPRESS STATION AT BOWL-
ing Green is only a short flight of stairs below Broadway. You don't
expect to suddenly see people sitting in the grassy concrete of Bowling
Green Park. The climb out of a subway usually takes all your effort.
New York becomes only an elevator ride at 120 Broadway. A hand
flushing nickels at the Automat. A nutted cheese sandwich at Chock
Full O' Nuts untouched by human hands. It was noon. The Custom
House stands sentry to the Atlantic. Bowling Green Park opens into
Lower Broadway, the financial district. And at noontime in the
financial district the business offices empty. Thousands of office
workers linger on the Wall Street sidewalk, their faces lifted toward
the sun. The men stand in groups of twos and threes. They talk
about the stock market, the world sticking up all around them, the
impossible mass of brick, limestone, steel, the great marble columns
of the bank buildings, glass. "You see what I'm trying to do," one
man, bareheaded, his blue suit unbuttoned, explained to his friends,
"I'm trying to lay my hands on a stock that'll pay off my house in
Bayside. I've got forty shares of Canadian oil now but it isn't enough.
You need a hundred, two hundred, to be safe." If you stand behind
people and listen, you can hear what they're saying.

Lower Broadway traffic knowingly detours Broad Street from
noon until two o'clock. Typists, secretaries, accountants, elevator

55

operators, fill Broad Street. Office workers sit on the steps of the Federal Building eating a lunch packed in Queens. Two sidewalk preachers flanked by American flags preach racial equality according to their own beliefs. "If you talk religion," the cop on Wall and Broad makes clear, "you can stay on that sidewalk twenty-four hours a day. The Supreme Court said that! But politics, cranks, nothing doing. Then the sidewalk is closed." But not to the insurance underwriters who gather in a great half-circle around the preachers, seemingly hoping to hear a good word. The brokers lean against the railing of the Stock Exchange, look east toward the sun. Broad Street stands in the shadow of its massive office buildings. But the sun floods the open areas, white shirts, cotton prints, red, blonde, black hair catching the tint. The egg salad sandwich with a coffee to go is digested. The sun rules Broad Street. A great Roman square. Nowhere in the world do so many people turn their faces to the sun as New Yorkers during lunch hour.

The east side of Seventh Avenue from 36th Street to 40th is deserted from twelve until one-thirty. The sun falls on the west side of the street. And there the thousands of garment workers who pour out of the loft buildings to swallow a hurried cafeteria lunch spend half their lunch time standing in the sun. The talk is about business, sometimes culture. "A woman reads the Kinsey report and a half hour later she's wondering if her husband is out fooling around with another woman. You can't apply statistics to a single individual, Morry, I don't care what the hell it is." The garment-cutters, gathering in the famous groups of twos and threes, blocking sidewalk traffic, making a spectacle talked about outside New York as that of a mass of robots, are simply standing in the sun. One short, squat man with a weak smile on his face applies to a trucking man for a job. The trucker swings racks of powder-blue pajamas out of his truck. "Are you around here every day?" he asks. "Every day," the man replies. "OK then, look for me here and if something comes up I'll know you're here."

The "virus" is around. It baffles the medical profession. "You don't know my trouble, Sid. The kids got it. Virus." And new jobs. "He wants to get more goods cut. Three hundred lots. I did it on my boss's time. He contracted me out. I got a box of cigars and overtime. But this guy wants new cutters, Sol, and good ones. He showed me his payroll. Ninety-seven hundred dollars for a head cutter. Seventy-three hundred for a cutter. That's with overtime. And he has plenty of it now. He wants me to go to work for him now. But I can't leave my job now, Sol. You don't know what you're walking into when you leave a job like mine." A lot of Yiddish is spoken. On the corner of 39th Street it's Italian. The models hurry out of the loft buildings in their sample suits, a collar flared with an extra inch of poodle cloth. They are seldom attractive, only the right height, and they rarely stand around. The police make no attempt to keep the garment workers moving, even when the men stand five, six, deep, blocking the sidewalk. How can you keep a man from breathing a little fresh air, sticking his face up into the sun?

Seventh Avenue, Broadway in the 30's, Wall Street, the big visible chunks of New York, furnish the evidence for the out-of-towner's judgment *ad nauseam:* New York is the craziest place on earth—New Yorkers are crazy themselves for being there. Fourteenth Street is also mad. On Saturday shoppers sweep twenty abreast down 14th Street from eleven until six-thirty—but only on the south side of the street. New Yorkers have a passion for choosing. Sidewalk peddlers line the sidewalk selling nylons, four pairs for a dollar. Slough! And the peddlers scurry from the police to the sanctuary of Union Square, the side streets of University Place. Woolworth's is packed. Buyers line up, fifteen in a row, patiently waiting their turn for a hot waffle ice cream sandwich. The frankfurter counter at Nedick's is three deep. Ohrbach's looks like VE Day in Piccadilly Circus. A detail of police handles the crowds swarming into Lane's, the women forming behind police barricades. Fire sale! Forty to seventy per cent off! Klein's dominates Union Square, the Harvard Five Foot shelf of ready-to-wear, its ticker tape of electric bulbs headlining bargains. Where do all these people live? How? And if they don't stop for a minute to look up into the sun, when do they stop? "These are people," the cop said, guarding the barricade. "Every one of them people. Christ, you'd wonder how they all figure out what to do."

Men tinkering with the "electronic age" shop on West Broadway, lower Greenwich Street, Canal, particularly Cortlandt Street. The walk is leisurely. The windows are filled with mysterious tubes that pluck sounds and pictures out of the sky. The hardware stores line up trays of GI surplus, the bookstores pornography. It's a sidewalk world, but no cafés, no demi-tasses. Only imagination, a screwdriver, a soldering iron, tubes and wire. I walked in to buy an LP sapphire needle at forty per cent off. A crew-cut announcer in black horn-rimmed glasses was asking a frightened housewife, who tried to shy away from the TV camera, "How much dirt would there be left in a hole 10 x 15 after you emptied it?" The clerk pointed to the model TV chassis. "If you like TV you like it. I like some of it." What about Cortlandt Street, they sell plenty of TV sets here. "You know they used to call Cortlandt Street 'gyp lane' but not anymore. This is an age of standard brands. This electrical stuff fascinates a lot of men," and he pointed to the racks of radios, amplifiers, tuners, recorders, aerials, speakers. "We get them from all over, the Village, Washington Heights, even Park Avenue, but mostly Riverside Drive. That's where you have the hi-fidelity bugs. Maybe you think I'm crazy but do you know what gets me, New York. Look at the George Washington Bridge!" A friend of mine calls it a marvel of engineering, I said. "Marvel! Do you know the George Washington Bridge moves twelve feet in the summer. Twelve feet! And what do you think New York did with the rock they dug out to make the subway?" I couldn't guess. "They built City College. You don't know where to stop looking in New York. Maybe it's because I'm studying engineering up at City." The engineers made New York, I volunteer. "Made it! Look at the highways surrounding New York. You can ride from Riverside Drive to Far Rockaway without a red light. Do you know they can dynamite a building right in the center of 46th and Madison and nobody hears a sound! Look at the way a new office building goes up. No men working. No steel lying around. And six months later you see the Lever Brothers building!"

The men double-park on Ninth Avenue waiting for their wives, who shop Paddy's Market. Most shoppers come by the IRT or out of the railroad flats that blanket Eighth, Ninth and Tenth Avenues. Paddy's isn't just one market but four blocks of midtown markets, predominantly Italian and Irish. Who can believe the mountain of food eaten daily in New York? How many cabbage farms are there? How many cattle on the hoof? The food in the supermarkets always looks as though it had been grown in glass jars, no earth, no air, only chemicals. But not in Paddy's Market. The beef looks as though it had just been slaughtered on Ninth Avenue. The Jersey vegetables are piled on the sidewalk, crumbs of earth still showing. And for an afternoon's shopping a housewife living on West 26th Street can walk the dozen blocks to Paddy's Market, feel close to the food she puts on her table, and incidentally, save money. Chicken at 29¢ a pound. Before you buy a dozen oranges, the Italian fruit man on 40th Street cuts into one, gives you the fruit to suck. How much are bananas at closing time? "Take it, four pounds for a quarter!"

Everybody knows you can go to Gimbel's and pay $5.95 for a summer cotton. And you can walk into Sak's Fifth Avenue and hand over $85.00 for a sport jacket. Or step into Delman's for Italian shoes. "If you have money," the woman picking a raincoat out of a pile told me, "nothing is expensive. But if you don't have money, then everything is expensive." I was telling her about the big bargain I saw in a thrift shop across the street on 70th and Third Avenue, an Oxford donegal jacket for $2.00. "And if you don't have the $2.00?" she asked. But the people don't shop the Third Avenue thrift shops to save money, only to run away from money, the bewildering red-lettered appeal for their dollar—"Sale! Selling Out!" Though bargains are a happy find. "There aren't any bargains," a woman told her friend, "only accidents. I'll tell you a rule I made up: if you see it, buy it, because when you need it, you can't buy it." She smiled for approval. "You're right," the friend agreed, "ten times right! Ten times I've taken the train from Washington Heights only to come back and find an empty hanger."

The thrift shops are run for charity. Society women who don't have to work stand behind the counters from ten to five and repeat over and over again the only sales line they know, "It's beautiful, it simply fits beautifully." The clothes and bric-a-brac are all donated. Brooks Brothers labels, Abercrombie & Fitch, Tripler hats, English weatherproofs, French handbags, evening gowns liquor-stained at Sherry's. What does a dollar buy? A worn Brooks Brothers sport jacket. "Are the people ashamed to buy second-hand clothes," I asked one volunteer worker in a black silk taffeta covered by a green smock as she took my dime for a French necktie. "No, they love it. We sell to everybody but mostly New Yorkers. It's the . . . the— where in the world do they have an equivalent for this?" and she pointed to the crowded shop, neatly dressed men and women bending over into cartons of used shoes, fingering dresses, trying on sport jackets in front of a cheval mirror. "London . . . Paris . . . no . . ." and her face became happy and thoughtful at being able to express itself, "you wouldn't have this anywhere else but New York. I think the thrift shops were invented by New Yorkers in lieu of a merry-go-round on every street corner."

Stand on the corner of 34th Street and Herald Square. Or plunge from 42nd Street into Times Square. Walk from Bowling Green to Columbus Circle. No man in a white jacket hands out brass rings for a free ride. In New York you pay your own fare. This wisdom a man in a raglan raincoat volunteered in Weiser's book store on Fourth Avenue. I picked up an old copy of *Dining in New York* on the 10¢ table. "Junk!" he said, pointing to the book, "nobody tells you what to do in this town. You do what's in your heart or die like a dog." I heard rumblings of the old Group Theater. Who tells you what's in your heart? "Not these kind of books. *Cue Magazine!* How many New Yorkers do you think read *Cue* or the fine type in the first pages of the *New Yorker?* It's all junk. Just for the beginners. You find your own weight soon enough. The Waldorf Starlight Room isn't a thousand times as big as the number of people who'd like to get in. But how many get in?" I don't know. "Yeow," he cried, turning away, looking up Fourth Avenue, "this is it, here, the real thing, this stone is New York stone! How many people do you think realize that? Do you want me to tell you something? Twenty-five years ago I took the train from Flatbush into New York and I haven't been back since. I remember it now and you won't find it in any book on Fourth Avenue—how different Brooklyn was from New York. Two worlds! One a dead doorstop. The other this—" He pointed to the racks and racks of books and then out of the door toward the Village and uptown toward 14th Street. Then he left to scan the 20¢ stall. Fourth Avenue is lined with books but bargains are rare, the prices as steady as Coca-Cola. The dealers know the market intimately but that doesn't prevent browsers from wandering in and out of the shops from 8th Street to 13th Street. The dealers remain taciturn, anonymous, buried in their lists. Browsing is an individual art. But if you look you can find bargains. I bought Edwin Markham's own Bible, two ancient volumes printed in Dublin, for 20¢. A rare copy of Casanova for 15¢, only one volume out of a twelve-volume edition, but it puts the lie to all the other translations.

Slip a dime into the turnstile of the East Side IRT at Grand Central. Choose the time, from four-forty-five to six-fifteen. Madison Avenue empties its typists; Fifth Avenue, its salesgirls. The advertising men who can afford it stop for two martinis—maybe three. The Biltmore has vis-à-vis tables set up in its lobby, an ensemble plays Continental music. The shop talk of editorial workers. The Roosevelt bar overflows. The gray-flannel-suiters walk to the East 70's. The lucky people hail cabs. The rest pour onto the platform of the 241st Street Bronx Express. An express train hurtles past every thirty seconds. And every thirty seconds the people hurl themselves in. "You know," a heavy-set, tired man on the Bronx Express philosophizes, "the more sardines a packer can pack into a tin the more money he's paid. Do you know why? Because the *olive oil* they put into the tins costs more than the sardines!" It doesn't seem possible that all the people on the swarming platform put up with the rush-hour crush fifty weeks a year. Two weeks in Asbury Park or the Catskills isn't enough, no matter how many desserts they serve. And what happens is this: the people bound for the Bronx, trapped, mashed, flung together, laugh. Really! The people in the trains, those left behind on the narrow platform, break out into smiles, joke, kid the attendants when they shove the passengers into the trains, forcing the bodies beyond the closing doors. It's happening to all of us! You have to learn to live with the subway or else you may find yourself exiled to some place like Levittown or Pough-keepsie. The subway is only one of the conditions exacted for living in New York.

How do you learn to live with a subway? Most people buy the *News, Mirror, Journal-American, Post, Times, Tribune* or *World Telegram*, bury their heads in the news. The others bury themselves in their thoughts. Look at the faces as the train rocks and hurls forward through the black tunnel. The subway system gives you the feeling of being there by a fiat of God. Who can still grasp the sub-way in terms of men digging dirt, carting away rocks? How many people are aware that it's a man who operates the trains, a man in the front car in a striped engineer's hat, not a remote push button. The eyes of the people in a subway car look outward, focusing on a point formed by the angle of both eyes, and there the people remain, seldom shifting for the entire ride. And at two in the afternoon a northbound BMT train from Brooklyn will look more profound than the Rembrandts at the Frick. But not all people experience themselves. Some talk. The veteran subway riders whisper to one another instead of trying to shout. What do the people talk about on the subway? What do the people talk about in Seattle? A blind man comes down the middle of a rushing Washington Heights "A" train singing an Irish ballad. Who gets a seat on the subway? Preg-nant women. The very old and wrinkled. And little children who are too young to stand and too old to be lap-carried. The rest of the population race toward the empty seat. You actually feel em-barrassed when you get up to give a seat to a woman precariously swaying on a Seventh Avenue Express train while trying to hold on to her 14th Street bargains.

And what is true on the subway is also true at 59th Street and Lexington Avenue, and that is what makes New York seem cold, distant, withdrawn, rushing headlong into nothingness. On the Fifth Avenue sidewalk the eyes seldom wander. On 34th Street the eyes are focused on the angle first-rate painters understand, outward, directed inward. It's partly a protective device, but mostly the genius of New York. Permit your eyes to wander. Walk down any

New York street. Even 24th Street changes at every instant. A church steeple, a loft building, a tenement fire escape, kids playing, delicatessens, frankfurters sold under orange umbrellas, ice cream carts, clothes hanging, TV aerials, endless tailor shops, buildings rising to crazy heights, many only three red-brick flights above the sidewalk; the sun breaking through throws shadows, tensions of form, no rules, at every turn some human effort squeezed into a cross-town street, until the eye is happy only to know its own existence.

Where can you sit if you're tired of pricing umbrellas at Sak's Fifth Avenue, window-shopping on 57th Street, looking at the flamboyant 57th Street women who come closest to one's notion of Balzac's courtesans, drifting in and out of the 57th Street art galleries, listening to one prospective buyer inquire fatuously, "But do you think he'll ever become famous?" A 57th Street Automat. And the Automats, the cafeterias are everywhere. The best buy is baked macaroni. And over the macaroni you see that the cafeterias are the café life of New York. Couples linger over cheese cake and coffee. No waiters rush your table. You don't feel compelled to drink an ounce of whisky every five minutes. Sit, take it easy, half the tables are empty. The decor is sometimes garish, sweeping murals of maidens sitting on top of mountain peaks. But in the afternoon the cafeterias offer a table to yourself, a chance to talk. "I'm tired, Ed. Tired and disgusted." "You take your work too seriously, Lil." "What else can I do but take it seriously? I get all the honeys. A fifteen-year-old girl wanted to come back and finish up at the P.S. She had a record and so I had to check up on her. Dope addiction and prostitution charges at thirteen-and-a-half. We found out that she was after more dope when the police intercepted a letter to her boy friend. He's seventeen, waiting trial for burglary. I had to see the kind of a house the kid lived in before I made any kind of a decision. Ed, so help me God, you know such places exist, still you don't believe it. How are they kept hidden so skillfully? We blind ourselves too quickly. The girl was a skinny little thing, blonde hair, almost no bigger than a full-grown baby, and she lay on one of those old-fashioned iron beds. No bedding, just an old sheet. The plaster was cracked, the walls dirty. I actually saw big rats coming out of a hole in the wall. New York! What the hell do you do, Ed? I called the Health Department, the Housing Inspector, the Police Department."

At four in the morning the demi-monde of Greenwich Village empty the bars and drink coffee on 8th Street. In the evening the men living alone cut into a plate of fried filet of sole. And if you don't like to sit in cafeterias, there is always Central Park. A stone wall runs around Central Park. But the trees grow naturally. And earth is earth. The benches along the pathway in the East 60's leading to the Zoo are crowded with people you'd expect to meet on a first-class deck. The Sherry-Netherland, the Pierre, the Savoy-Plaza, are just across the street. The pigeons grow tired of eating and at intervals swoop away to rest on the branches of the trees. A class of Negro children trudge in broken formation across the concrete walk but as they reach the grass they break ranks and rush toward the swings, dropping on their stomachs to shoot cattle rustlers sneaking up from Central Park West. The children come in groups, teachers leading the formations. But one little girl was trudging along the grass with her younger sister, the older girl clutching a brown paper grocery bag. "You don't like the Park! You don't like it! Then why do you make me bring you?" The accent was Ninth Avenue. On Ninth Avenue in the 50's the street play is simple. The children beat one another over the head, kick their bodies. The boys wrestle on the sidewalk, the little girls run screaming in and out of doorways. Together they leap on the cars parked on 53rd Street, hurl one another to the sidewalk. At the pond in Central Park I saw little boys in Brooks Brothers suits sailing their boats. The shoreline was Fifth Avenue in the 70's. "Mother, mother," one boy called and his mother dutifully rose from her *New Yorker*. "Mother, come here, look!" and he showed her a dead fish he and his friend had retrieved from the pond. In the 80's on the lawn at the rear of the Metropolitan Museum the children play intricate ball-throwing games, gather in storytelling circles. Negroes and whites are in some of the groups. The little girls all look like future Greenwich Village bar-stool beer drinkers. The boys are magnificently dressed, usually a three-button sport jacket with a natural shoulder cut. And you can see how the loose, flopping men you used to know at college got their way of wearing clothes.

What do people do in the Park? Newspapers are carried but seldom read. Some wander to look at the caged animals in the Zoo. The two gorillas succeed in making you stop and wonder. The open-air cafeteria attracts Europeans, Rolleiflex cameras. Fifth Avenue mothers show off their childbearing bodies in tailored cottons as they parade their babies around the seals. Three girls stand on a mound of earth taking snapshots of each other. Some ladies bring roller skates and skate up and down the quarter-mile of concrete set aside for roller skaters. Horses come strangely down the bridle path. And a brother and sister come to the Park to talk it out in the open. "Some people—you wonder how in the hell God let them live. How did air get into their throats at the beginning!" And the girl on the bench turns to her brother and asks him, "Why did I have to marry the bastard? Why me?"

Trees grow on Riverside Drive, pathways lead down to the Hudson River. The twisting walks remind you of Edinburgh. The sweep of Riverside Drive is like Princess Street. Park benches line the entire length of Riverside and in the afternoon the pigeons are as well fed as their Central Park brothers. Mostly old people seem to live on Riverside now, the New Yorkers who lifted themselves out of rail-road flats and who are now holding on to their ceiling rentals. You can pay $67.00 a month for a one-room efficiency, hang yellow pueblo cloth drapes, or else take seven rooms for $285 and over-look the Hudson. What do the women talk about who spend their lives riding elevators? "Without the park I couldn't live!" On almost every park bench you hear it repeated. "Without the park I couldn't live!" Without Riverside Drive Park life would not be possible. Across the street, West End and Broadway are one great hunk of uniformity. The shops don't vary from 72nd Street up, block after block of butcher shops, fruit, vegetables, canned goods, dry cleaners, shoe repair, dress shops, neckties, delicatessens. No second-hand books, antiques, thrift shops: everything new, stamped, cut from the same steel die, endlessly repeated. At one o'clock the women of the West 80's gather for lunch in front of Schrafft's. The

inside dining room is one vast mass of voices. The women dress in
the exacting standards that meet the general level of too much coat,
too thickly applied pancake makeup, unreal blue-black hair. Stand
on the Broadway sidewalk. Watch the women wait for a taxi, a late-
comer for strawberry shortcake. The women can't take their eyes off
one another. And the only ones who escape are those who were made
beautiful. And for those who can't get into Schrafft's there are the
park benches set in the middle of Broadway, islands with green grass
growing. The traffic goes both ways and in the middle the people
who find themselves ending their lives in a Broadway apartment
house sit on the green benches and lift their faces toward the sun.

The East Side has no park benches, only trees held up by baling
wire. On the corner of East 66th and Second Avenue two slim trees
planted in the cement stand alone against the block-long, block-
wide, all-window, shining white-brick Manhattan House. The East
Side is New York. It doesn't pretend to be Shaker Heights, Ohio,
or, say, Wilshire Boulevard in Los Angeles. On 75th and Madison a
French poodle carries an LP record between its jaws. Men stroll by
in black derbies. Madison at 75th looks like a closed reservation.
No mistake in clothing, particularly in the men. The high style for a
man is a tight-fitting suit, a black derby. You needn't look further
than the black-sling leathery pumps, the $2.95, 66 gauge, 15 denier
nylons to know an East Side New York woman. And the eye on
Madison Avenue is focused on the same point the subway riders
concentrate all their attention. It's New York! Why? Until you've
learned why you're just a small-town boy running away from Denver
culture.

Turn off Madison into a midtown auction gallery. Two attendants
in green uniforms bring out a portrait of a woman and frame it
against a backdrop of red velvet. "Modigliani, oil on canvas, signed,"
the auctioneer announces. The audience sits taut waiting for the
opening bid. This is the arena of legend and big-money culture.
"One thousand dollars to open." An appreciative hush from the
audience. Two thousand is bid. The price immediately jumps to
$2,500. Then $3,000. The audience bobs like a prizefighter, trying to locate the bidders. A series of quick $100 raises and the

Modigliani is knocked down to a gray-suited elderly man who hands his card to an attendant. Renoir, Utrillo, Picasso, Chagall, Dufy, Rouault, Vuillard draw big, fashionable crowds. What do you see? People looking for bargains in art—a Picasso to hang on a thirty-foot living room wall. "I got it! I got it!" a woman cries to her circle of friends. "I got the Dufy!" You suspect this is New York society as you see the stiff consciousness of art-struck movie stars, the high-collar blue-striped tab shirts of seeming connoisseurs, the custom-needled people who settle back to enjoy what the world has already given sanction to.

Look at New York. Ride slowly in a cab across the Triborough Bridge as it runs parallel to the East River. Stare at the skyline as Harry did on his way to La Guardia Airport. What do you think about New York back home before you're ready to make the trip, I asked him. "You think of all the things you're going to do. Carnegie Hall. Plays. Parties. Greenwich Village—" And when you get here? "You check into your hotel. Wash up. Take the elevator down to the lobby. And then you're hit by the sidewalk. All those goddamn buildings staring at you. How do you stand it? It's no good, New York. It makes a man run a rat race!"

Max calls on the telephone and recites what he's going to do for the week. See *The Young and Damned*, the matinee of *Venus Observed*, hear a quartet at Town Hall, go to Esther's weekly party on Christopher Street. Applaud! Open the door on Esther's party. Smoke. A black wrought-iron table supports two bottles, a gallon of American Chianti. Pineapple cut in strips, diced according to *Woman's Day*. Two studio couches, a settee, half a dozen Swedish chairs, manage to fit in most of the people. The door opens. Esther plays the hostess. "This is John! He paints pictures." A whisper goes around the room. Kleemann, a girl repeats, Perls, Rosenberg, finally—Wildenstein? Scan the coming attractions at Carnegie Hall, you want to tell Max, the list at Town Hall. Cleveland is a dreary rat race, Pittsburgh, Los Angeles. But not New York. You can't race after culture in New York. The odds are always on the infinite. And that is why when a New Yorker loves New York, he really loves the city. He understands that the competitive system has broken down. You curiously feel the city accessible. You don't have to prove yourself by attending every recital at Town Hall. The *Times* advertises a Washington Square flat at $486 a month, a three-room Hudson Street cold-water flat at $17.00. A writer makes $400 a week filling the balloons in comic books. A publisher may advance you $500 for two years' work on a novel. What's in between? A 10¢ beer at Fugazzi's. Visit a friend in a West Broadway loft. Climb four flights up a wooden stairway to a small square room. Sit in an old cane chair and talk over a quart of beer as he works on a painting. Watch him poking colors onto the canvas. The paints are on a wooden board. Brushes stick up out of an empty milk bottle. You only have to solve the problem of your own life.

At times New York is bleak. You don't have couples lingering on the sidewalk being photographed by *Life* as they kiss down the length of a Parisian street. Only the obvious honeymooners hold hands on New York streets. Couples sometimes neck openly in Washington Square Park. Girls are rarely kissed on Fifth Avenue, Madison, Park, Riverside, only for a formal hello or good-bye. Seldom do you see men flirting on a bus, a subway, even in Central Park, or girls responding. You have to stand on your head to find a cruising prostitute. The saddest faces to be seen are the sailors and soldiers who swarm into Greenwich Village looking for life. Where can you take a visitor from Paris or Buenos Aires except to Radio City? New York life is lived in apartments. And if you have no apartment, no friends, then you have the etching of a furnished room in Chelsea. Cold. Crazy. Who's in, who's out, who wins, who loses, you say. Where do you touch bottom?

You don't touch bottom. You live out your life. On West 111th Street. Or East 95th Street. Two rooms on West 10th Street. I took my little friend Kate for a walk across the Williamsburg Bridge. The Lower East Side fascinated her when she learned she could buy a dress cheaper on Rivington Street than on 14th. Her father unloads the South American freighters of the Grace Line, pays $14.00 a month for a four-room cold-water flat on West Street crowded by two warehouses. In the middle of the Williamsburg Bridge you're high enough to look down on all of New York, particularly the

Lower East Side, the great ugly mass formed by Houston Street, the East River, Broadway and Delancey Street, the dense walkups. "These are the slums of New York, aren't they, Zus, these buildings," she asked, pointing downward, over the railing, into the windows looking out on the bridge. Yes, I said. She looked again at the unbroken line of black-sooted flats. "You know, these slums are worse than the slum I live in." But she said it without satisfaction or dismay, only with the education of a New Yorker.

The Burial

EDITH MADE THE FIRST BREAK. "I HATE THIS APART-
ment," she said to Dora at supper. "I hate it and we have to get out."

"But where can we move to?" Dora asked.

"I don't care. But we have to get out of this house."

"Out of Brooklyn?" Dora asked.

"Out of this house!"

"But where—?" Dora asked again. She too had been reading the
apartments-for-rent column in the *Times*. And there were no apartments, only mansions, wood-burning fireplaces for movie actresses
to toast marshmallows in—winding stairways that led to master
chambers and sweeping views of the East River.

"We'll check the papers and leave our names with some agents."

"But they have lists a mile long."

"The lists don't mean anything," Edith insisted. "It's luck.
Somebody goes out, somebody has to move in. We'll find a place."

On the day their father died and they rode to the cemetery in
black hired cars Dora knew from her sister Edith they would move
from their railroad flat in Williamsburg and it was nothing Edith
had said, but just because she knew, just as she had known her
father was dying when her cheek turned cold at his moan and she
ran into his dark, windowless bedroom. The death of their father
came after long months of his moaning, keeping them awake, tired,

70

exhausted for the morning subway ride across the East River. Dora and Edith were stuck in that dark, bleak, humorless neighborhood across the Williamsburg Bridge where it was difficult to think of any other kind of world. This is the way the world is, would be the daily complaint. It was like that part of a city seen from a train window, that always looks as though there is no escape from it, grim, rotten, sunless. The old man made his money in a cigarmaker's store where his fingers became stained wrapping the moist tobacco leaves. And when his heart couldn't hold his body, he gave up wrapping the moist leaves and stretched out in his dark, windowless bedroom. He would lay all day in bed thinking of the little money he had deposited in the Williamsburg Savings Bank, wondering how long the money would hold him, seldom of the long days ahead when he would lie in his blue Saturday suit and not be able to move his toes nor have a voice in the rolling of the moist tobacco leaves. Death didn't frighten him, for life was making it more and more difficult for him to live. He hung on though and the two girls watched their father die.

He had become in his illness a stranger in the long narrow railroad flat. Dora and Edith kept to their rooms and he lay in his room. The girls seldom visited him at night. What could they talk about? And what did they talk about when he was still going to the cigar store? Dora would go straight into the kitchen when she came home and tend to the pots on the stove making the same thick, heavy, sweet-smelling gravy and fatty chunks of chuck roast her mother had made. Edith would sit in her partitioned-off bedroom off the long hallway and look at her tired face and wonder how beautiful girls were born. And after the thick fatty chunks of chuck roast had been eaten and lemon squeezed into a glass of tea, the old man would sit and look at the four walls and the two girls would scrub the kitchen. There was little break in the routine, no change in the heavy walnut furniture bought when the tenement still showed traces of the original red brick. The girls often thought of buying new furniture, but for what, for whom? And the father lingered, though life had completely left him. Dora and Edith never stopped looking after him, their distance never dissipated into forgetfulness. They had long ago set up that happy family balance, unspoken but knowing, and then conveniently forgotten, that made peace possible in the house. The girls didn't criticize their father for his failings; he didn't yell at them for not being an exact image of his dead wife: they all lived as though they were happy. Nobody had a complaint. But in dreams:

Edith wanted to marry. Once she lived out a dream. "What the hell—" she said in her high, throaty, scratching Brooklyn voice and withdrew $600 from her account at the Williamsburg Savings Bank and off she traveled. To Florida where the sun shone all day long and men walked around in white dinner jackets and the whole stretch of the white, green spiralling sky-scraped beach looked as though man had made his happy dream come true. Edith took a room for $15.00 a day with a view of the mysterious ocean and a little gadget that regulated the temperature. She changed her clothes four times a day until her supply began running low. Her plan was simple: to catch a man. She caught only one man. The man smiled at her in the lobby of her $15.00-a-day hotel and she smiled back and later in the evening he took her to a magnificent night club that made her feel West End Avenue in the full of her hand every time she lifted her glass of French wine but then at the end of the evening he casually slipped the check toward her end of the table . . . .

Dora had no mighty plan for catching a man: somewhere in the world there was a man for her and they would meet and she would be safely married. If it didn't happen today, it would happen tomorrow. For what other reason was she born?

The day after the funeral Dora made a great fuss of looking at the pots on the stove and Edith went into her bedroom. They ate in silence, neither daring to break the continuity. What could they say? "Pa is dead, let's go dance in the street!" But day by day the dinners became less complicated. Tuna fish began to appear on the table. Fried salami and eggs. Boiled frankfurters . . . .

The girls both knew their apartment was a place to die in, to end a life, not begin a life. It stood past the middle of the block, darkened by a warehouse and supported on either side by two rotting tenements. The street was mean and ugly. At night the foghorns made it still more isolated. Garbage was thrown on the sidewalk. It was a place that people find themselves in with no way of getting out.

They both began to dread the long lonely walk down the dark street at night. Purses had been snatched in the neighborhood. Gangs of boys roamed loose, roughing up girls. The Williamsburg Bridge rose above it, dimly lighted and over the sky hung the lights of New York, the orange glow from Times Square. They could see the whole of the city if they walked on the bridge. But they never walked out of the neighborhood onto the bridge and midway across to look down on the East River and beyond the East River, the completely fabulous sight of Manhattan.

Edith refused to accept defeat. She got up an hour early in the morning to get the *Times* and phone all the available listings. They spent Sunday looking at apartments on the upper West Side of Broadway, big ugly rooms with fake kitchens and enormous rents. But out of it all, the constant phoning and pleading with superintendents, the two girls began to get the feel of a new world, a world of people who lived safely in well-constructed buildings with doormen who said good morning and good evening, who helped you with packages, warm-lighted rooms with expensive lamps and rich carpeting—it all existed, for they passed the buildings every Saturday and Sunday, their hands almost fingering the cold limestone, brushing up against it as though begging for admittance. They could afford to pay a sizeable rent, not too much, but much more than the $22.00 a month their railroad flat cost. And as the weeks went by, they began putting away the rent money they would have paid had they been living in a legitimate apartment, and the sum grew.

The father had been forgotten now in this new world. Though they sometimes asked themselves why he never wanted to move out of Williamsburg to the airy tree-lined streets of Flatbush, or even, as they desired, the hard streets of Manhattan, upper Broadway where the outpouring of people on the sidewalk, the lighted, satin dress shops, the mink coats and orange crates, the big apartment houses, was the world.

Dora and Edith took to eating out one meal a week. They would meet in Manhattan and take a subway to West 86th Street and walk until they found an expensive restaurant. Edith began to buy new clothes. And Dora changed. Her face had a glowing smile. The office rumor was that she had a man, for all things are solved by a girl getting a man. But on the dark Sunday evenings when their search for an apartment ended in a final *no* and they crossed the Williamsburg Bridge to leave the dark tunnel for another dark tunnel, the long, narrow, dark rooms of their railroad flat that emptied one into the other like a black night, then they felt the loss of their father. Pa is dead. Ma is dead. The house is dead. We need a new house! It didn't seem possible to Dora and Edith that there wasn't one tiny corner of one of the big imposing buildings on Broadway that was free and open for them to move into.

The cold flat was silent. The phone seldom rang. No calls from real estate agents. Dora and Edith seldom spoke. What could they say? What did their father ever say to them that they could remember like poetry? But in that deep, still, soundless world of dreams Edith wished for a man to come down the dark tunnel and carry her off into the daylight. Even if it meant leaving her sister alone. And in fancy she saw herself putting aside sums of money her husband freely gave her to help Dora out with, laying the money in a carefully sealed white envelope discreetly on Dora's kitchen table, feeling a great pity for Dora, for Dora would never know what it was like to lay down next to a man and feel his leg cross over yours and take you around to make you sink back deep down into the bed and then open wide so that he was all in you and would never want to be anywhere else.

Dora had been a mother to her dead father for so long that she felt she would go on being a mother, even to a new man, a living man. The sisters never wondered why neither had dates. But they knew dates would begin once they were out of Williamsburg. The free evenings now were completely given over to hunting for an apartment. How could a prospectful man come down the dark street and look at the ugly warehouse and then walk up their wooden stairs to knock at their door illuminated by a dull red bulb in the hallway? And the furniture, now heavy with the candles of two dead. The sagging sofa that sank to the floor. Where could the date sit? Where? They'd have to go out of the house and around the corner to where? They had to move! It became their whole life. The food lay tasteless on the table. They made no attempt to fix up the flat. Let it rot of its own accord. Dora was the mother and she suffered the most. She knew Edith had ideas in the clouds. And like a mother she suffered for her baby lost in the clouds. How can a mother insist to her baby, there are no clouds, only this, the earth and if the earth is Williamsburg . . .

But all this went on in silence. The only realities were the ads that read: "Two rooms, bath, kitchenette, west of Central Park, $180 a month on lease." There were cheaper flats but only the lucky got them. Dora and Edith were always too late. One day the lawyer in Dora's office said to her, "Why don't you stop up and see the superintendent in my building. The rents aren't expensive and people are always moving out. Leave your name with the super. Tell him that you know me."

Dora immediately hurried to the building, an eighteen-story apartment house looking south toward midtown Manhattan. The superintendent was a nice old man. He took Dora's name and promised to call. The promise to call gave their phone a new importance. Dora and Edith lived by every ring and didn't dare leave the apartment at night. One night the superintendent of the building did call. He had a vacancy and would Dora like to look at it?

Dora and Edith were afraid to see the night end, a new day begin. A thousand things could happen that might lose the apartment for them. A relative of the owner stranded without an apartment, a large bribe, a remembered friend, there was no reason why they should be picked, why the phone number in Williamsburg should have been dialed. Dora and Edith couldn't sleep through the night. When it was daylight they dressed and took a subway to upper Broadway.

The ceilings were white and the walls painted Nile-green and a doorman stood in front of the building and a man in a uniform ran the elevator and the bathroom had an enormous tub and the kitchen a refrigerator, the windows of the living room looked out on people sitting by Chinese lamps.

"How much is it?" Dora asked and she stood like a bride, her whole life to be lived once the glass exploded under the foot of her husband.

"It's cheap for an apartment like this—$76.00—"

"We'll take it," Dora said without hesitation, though $76.00 was $54.00 more than what they were paying now. But what was $54.00 when the world rose eighteen floors above the ground.

Dora signed the lease that afternoon and the apartment belonged to them for three years.

Edith wanted to close the door on the railroad flat and leave everything but their clothes. "It can all go to hell," she told Dora. But Dora argued for her pots and together they picked out a few books, some silver, the candelabra, family pictures, old letters that they read and then tossed into the big cardboard carton they had gotten from the grocer on the corner. Dora kept a few of the letters "just in case." When the movers came there was nothing to move except a few cartons and the clothes. The rest remained where it had been placed years ago, buried in the flat. And when Dora closed the door she felt as she did when the dirt began to fall on her father's coffin and the sound of the gravel on the wood told her that he could never rise again. It's terrible to be dead, and after an inexplicable shudder she said, but with this kind of dying it's all right. She closed the door and the lock snapped. Dora and Edith walked down the dark hallway and down the stairs into the street to the mover's truck.

The first weeks in the new apartment were spent in cleaning up after the painters, the floor scrapers who left a coating of dust on all the woodwork. But Dora loved the work, especially scraping the streaks of paint off the white tile in the bathroom until the walls were immaculate. Dora and Edith went to Herald Square and bought a green rayon shower curtain and a deep tufted cotton shower mat. The money came out of their dowery, the Williamsburg Savings Bank bankbook that Edith opened one night at supper.

"We've got $1100 saved," Edith told Dora, "plus whatever money we both have privately."

"Eleven hundred dollars," Dora repeated.

"But that doesn't mean we should start right in buying furniture," Edith said, repeating all of the advice given to her by the girls at the office. "We'll have to look and look. But whatever we buy, let's right now decide to buy the best. There's no bargain in cheap furniture." And they both knew from their Williamsburg days that the best was measured against the $1100. For how can you spend what you don't own? But now, with $1100! Every Thursday night when the stores stayed open until nine and all day Saturday, Dora and Edith would sweep through acres of furniture in Herald Square, Fifth Avenue, admiring fireside chairs, feeling fabrics, asking questions, turning tags for prices, shrugging off what was too expensive, and in the end they resisted every impulse to buy what they always fancied and filled their living room with chairs of puffed-up down, furniture safely dated in the nineteenth century. The living room floor they covered with a sea-green carpet and to be modern Edith bought a blond mahogany cocktail table and placed on it a ceramic ash tray with an exaggerated nude traced in Pascin lines they had picked up one night in the Village after meeting some girls for dinner on West 4th Street.

Dora took over the kitchenette. But the small space disappointed her. She had no room to turn, no cupboard space for her big heavy black pots. The kitchenette was enclosed in a closet with folding doors, built to heat a pot of coffee, slice a cheese sandwich, not to stir the thick fatty chunks of chuck roast they had grown up on. "Get rid of the pots," Edith suggested again. "We don't have to eat so heavy." But Dora finally thought of driving nails into the wall above the refrigerator and the pots hung in a neat row. "It looks functional now," Dora said, using a word she had heard the salespeople repeat endlessly, as though furniture wasn't supposed to be functional. The apartment began to look lived in. And when Dora hung the block linen floral drapes they had ordered at an expensive Lower East Side drapery store, the apartment was finished. "All that remains now is to live out a life," Edith said to Dora, and she smiled when she said it.

Edith bought a pair of platform shoes. Dora treated herself to a new pyramid coat. At night, after scrubbing down the kitchenette, they would walk up Broadway as far as 96th Street, window shopping, getting ideas for the house, picking up delicacies of lox, smoked carp, hot bagels, hard salami, joking with the clerks who wrapped the olives, weighed the red pistachios for the silver nut tray. The clerks, the waiters when they stopped in for a corned beef sandwich, a chocolate egg cream soda, were the only people they found themselves speaking to. There were no other people. They knew no one on Broadway. Only the faces they began to recognize on their nightly walks. "Where do the people go to?" Edith said to Dora, and then she answered her own question. "They live in apartments like us. On Riverside Drive. West End. Broadway. We're like them." "Do they know each other, do you think," Dora asked, "the way we knew everyone on the block in Williamsburg?" "Some, maybe. But look at the windows. A whole city lives in one building."

Edith didn't like to be alone. Nor did she like the nightly walks that were beginning to depress her. In Williamsburg you were afraid of gangs of boys who might throw you down on the sidewalk, but here on Broadway—and she didn't want to say what she was afraid of.

"Let's give a party," Edith said one night to Dora. "The place is all fixed up for a party."

"A house warming party," Dora said. "That's a good idea."

Edith made all the plans for the party. And Dora baked the heavy honey cakes her mother used to make for the high holidays. The smell of the honey cakes filled the apartment with a remembrance of Williamsburg, the old Peerless stove red hot, their mother tasting the food but never eating it, not once did they ever see her sit down to a full meal. All of her life was lived in the kitchen of the railroad flat, on the orange crate in front of the building. She seldom spoke to the girls, never to the neighbors. It was a rare silence, unbroken until she died. And when she died she was forgotten. But now the smell of the honey cake that Dora learned to bake watching her mother stir the sugar in a heavy wooden bowl made the room warm with a remembrance of the two dead old people.

"What do you think pa would have said about this?" Dora asked Edith, and swept her hand in a circle around the sea-green carpet.

"The rent would have killed him. And for him to get on the subway and ride out to Brooklyn every day—never."

"The place looks nice," Dora said, settling back on the couch.

The napkins were laid out. Knives, forks, spoons, nuts, candy, the honey cake sliced, a bottle of whisky stood on the cocktail table.

"Nice, nice," Edith said. The stage was set. It was just a stage set. God, when would she stop smiling, always agreeing? The damn dreams coming lately, draining her body. A sea-green carpet they needed. Why the party? Just to have people over the house. Who ever visited? You made promises and never went. People lived so far from one another, down the subway steps. It took all your strength just to ride the IRT twice a day. But God, she didn't want to be like her mother, sit on an orange crate nodding her head. So they would have the party. Eat the honey cake. Pour the whisky bottle empty. Ice cubes from the refrigerator. Crumbs on the sea-green carpet. And then the relatives to come and say, look at the furniture, the drapes, the lamps, their tongues deep down in their throats—for two girls to have done all this! Could she tell it to Dora? How crazy it was for two girls to buy furniture like they were married—honeymooners just beginning an apartment. A life together. Shop! Shop! Shop! For what? For who? To look at four freshly painted walls. No wonder their mother never talked. It must have all been inside of her! How she must have dreamt on the water of the ocean. And then to die in Williamsburg. In a dark dirty house in a dark room behind windows that looked out on a warehouse. People lived in New York like slaves at the bottom of a salt mine. Edith looked at her sister Dora on the couch. Dora wouldn't ever complain out loud either. God made the world for beautiful people. Was it just having a beautiful face, hips that curved opening out? The apartment would soon be filled with people drinking and she could see the faces of her relatives staring at her and oh, no, now she was sorry she had thought about it, sorry and sick, her face showed it, her eyes staring at the tall Chinese lamp on the leather tooled table.

"Edith—?" Dora asked, for she had noticed the change in her sister's face.

"A gas pain," Edith said.

"We won't serve the tuna fish for the party," Dora said. "Too many people complain about the oil in tuna fish. It's not the real fish oil. It just lays on your heart."

"No, we won't serve the tuna fish," Edith said. "Just the honey cake." And Dora shivered when she heard Edith say "just the honey cake" because she knew, just as she had known her father was dying when she heard his weak moan, and just as she had known that Edith wanted to move out of Williamsburg even before she said a word about moving, she knew Edith had been looking at the four walls, the bedroom without a man, the old life, the new life. Life was life. What could she say to Edith, who wanted to dance in the street like she did when she was a little girl to the organ grinder's music in the playground under the bridge by the Navy Yard.

"The world—" Dora began to say.

"Yes—" Edith asked.

"The world," Dora said, "is a beef frankfurter boiled eight minutes," and she hoped her sister would laugh at her joke.

Edith didn't laugh. The door bell rang and she got up from the couch taking a last helpless look at the living room. The lamps were on in all of the corners and they gave the soft, expensive look she liked. Not like the one bulb hanging from the center of the kitchen ceiling throwing a white light on the rotting woodwork. The paint couldn't cover age. What did her Aunt Gittell once say? There's only one blessing good people have, the years show the real character of a person, it's written on their face. And wasn't it written on her face that she wanted to lay down twisting in bed, to fix up more than two rooms, run the washing machine down in the basement. What did people read on her face? The door would open now, her Aunt Gittell, Sam, what would they read, talk about, because she knew how things were, the party would be talked about that night, on the subway, in bed. Edith and Dora, did you notice, two girls alone, so nice, but such a shame—. Edith opened the door to let in Rose, her worker at the office. Edith had decided to mix the company, some from the family, some from the office.

"It's beautiful! Beautiful!" Rose didn't expect for a minute to see what was laid out before her eyes, the sea-green carpet, the new gleaming mahogany, the lamps that could only be expensive. She sat down on the couch next to Dora, repeating, "You made it beautiful. Just beautiful."

"A drink?" Edith asked.

"I need one. The place has taken away my breath."

"You like it?" Dora asked.

"I love it," Rose said.

The doorbell kept ringing and Edith saw each face light up, taken back by surprise. Her relatives couldn't keep their hands off the sofa, feeling the quality, the stuffing, foam rubber, trying to add up the price of the lamps. And the apartment made all of the conversation. Nothing else was talked about. Edith and Dora repeated how they had saved their money, planning to move into a new apartment, " . . . and whatever difference there was in the rent we were paying in that hole in Williamsburg and what we expected to pay, we put into the bank. Now Fifth Avenue has all the money."

The party broke up late. Dora didn't go to sleep until she washed all the dishes, carpet-swept the floor. Once roaches took hold of an apartment it was hard to drive them out. It had been a good party, Dora and Edith decided lying in bed awake. No complaints. The apartment was a success. Edith knew how some of the girls in her office lived. Girls who came from nowhere out of the West, some from the South, just to live in New York. They worked five days a week, rented a little boxed-off room for $8.00 a week, and why they did it she didn't know. Not one of them wanted to ride to the moon; marry a prince. They didn't talk about anything extraordinary. What kind of life could they have in the rooms? She shivered the first time she saw Rose's room on West 22nd Street in the back off a dirty carpeted stairway. She couldn't understand why Rose was so proud to say, this is it, this is my room. And Rose acted as though she *lived* in the room, throwing off her hat, picking up a nail file, clothes hanging from a little line attached to the radiator. What was Rose's room? What was her father's room? What was their room? What was any room? Did pa ever think about their rooms in Williamsburg? Or ma? She had heard some talk about how important the first years of your life were, how what happened then might be responsible for everything that happened later. But that wasn't fair! The world can be a stinking flight of stairs that led into long dark rooms and a sick father and furniture that stunk from kerosene, yet you rode the subway, went to work, looked at people, ate lunch, chewing down a cream cheese sandwich and you didn't feel anything except that you were just what you were. She never felt otherwise. Maybe it was Broadway. The buildings rose tall, big, the people all looked important but you didn't know who belonged to who. Buy a bagel. By a chocolate soda. Buy a five pound salami. Buy a dress reduced $8.00. Big bargain. All she and Dora did on Broadway was buy, buy, buy. Buy, pile up junk, shop, eat, go to the toilet.

In the morning Dora went over the apartment again, wiping away the finger marks on the tables. The linen drapes had been fingered by everyone at the party but luckily there weren't any smudge marks. And no drinks had spilled on the carpet. Before Dora and Edith left for work, the apartment looked as shining as it did when Edith opened the door to let in Rose. It was strange, Dora thought, how just mere cleaning seemed to bring out the furniture, make it look almost human. Maybe that was because of all the work that went into cleaning. A clean house. The room did look alive after you dusted, mopped, wiped away the soot. For Dora the party had been a success but she knew Edith hadn't slept most of the night. Edith had words inside of her. And when you lay awake at night the words don't leave your head for a minute.

The elevator door opened on the main floor. Dora and Edith turned toward the subway. The clouds were down with a low wet mist making the buildings look big, bare, distant. Their building was the tallest on the street and now they could see the top of it hidden in the clouds. The steam would soon begin, something they had never known in Williamsburg. The cold flat had no steam, only the oil burner. Both girls remembered the long cold walks to the end of the street to go down in the cellar where a little Italian man sold pieces of wood and cans of kerosene. The kerosene kept the flat warm. Some people complained about the steam heat. The steam dried out the room leaving your throat raw, sore in the morning. The steam came through pipes. The elevator rode on cables. The subway train came now out of the black tunnel on electric rails. A man steered the train all day long. Edith held on to the swaying train as the cars swerved for the long stretch into Chambers Street. The city was wound up like a baby in pain. Where did people walk freely? What could you do if you had an hour to spend between an appointment? It lay on you like the smell of kerosene. Unless you had a definite person to see, a movie to watch, a friend to visit, a dress to buy, the rest was brick, stone, shifting people, black as the long nights below the bridge.

Edith refused to give any more parties. The first party was the last party. Edith began sitting in the bedroom as she had done in the cold flat in Williamsburg. The house became still. The lamps gave a dull yellow light on the sea-green carpet. One night Dora shivered when she thought she heard the coughing of her dead father. She tried to make lavish meals of stuffed fish, intricate goulashes, home-baked bread, the hot crustless apple pies her mother was so proud of making, anything to try and get Edith to feel that the apartment was her home. Edith didn't talk about the party, nor did she say why she didn't want to give any more parties. If only she had a man, Dora would say. But a man had to come his legs churning the waves as a fellow had once swum up to her at Brighton Beach ducking her under the water, teaching her to swim with his hand resting on her breast. Edith had such little breasts then.

Edith made the first break.

"Let's get away from Broadway," she said to Dora at supper.

"Away from Broadway," Dora said, as though the question had never been on her mind.

"The neighborhood isn't for us," Edith said.

"But where will we move to?" Dora asked, and it seemed as though the day hadn't ended yet when they rode out to the cemetery to bury their father.

"Anywhere. Maybe the Village."

"But you can't find an apartment in the Village. It's impossible. There aren't any vacancies down there."

"We'll look. We found this place, didn't we? And we've got all of our furniture now. We can just take it with us. There won't be any new expenses."

"Take it with us—the furniture." Dora shivered. Didn't they leave everything behind when the lock snapped on the door of the railroad flat and she heard the gravel falling on the wooden-covered body of her dead father whose head and feet and shoulders were being covered by dirt.

"Maybe we can put an exchange ad in the *Times*."

"But we have a lease—"

"The lease can be broken—"

Dora didn't want to argue. The lease could be broken. Who wouldn't want an apartment on the eighteenth floor with a view of the river, the big buildings sticking up in the air shining at night?

"First we'll have to start looking for a place in the Village," Dora said, "before we say anything to anybody about breaking the lease."

"It's luck," Edith said. "Somebody goes out, somebody has to move in. We'll find a place."

Poor People

I WAS WALKING ALONG EAST BROADWAY EATING A pineapple ice that I had bought on Rutgers Street when my friend, Abe Geller, pointed to two old Jewish men sitting on a stoop talking to one another. "I'll bet they have a story to tell," he said to me.

"So what?" I said. "All people have a story to tell."

"It's life—those two men are real life. Nobody writes about life anymore."

Life—that was a word to silence me.

"Look," I told him, "I'll make up a story about those two men. Will that be life?"

"No," he said. "That isn't real life."

"What is real life?" I asked him.

"Real life is people."

Oh.

Two weeks later I gave Abe this story to read.

"We people have our problems," said Mr. Phillips to his friend, Leon Sandler, an old retired hatmaker who had long ago stopped listening to his friend and who, because of his profound silence, was looked upon by Mr. Phillips as his closest friend on earth, the one person he could trust with whatever high thoughts he would permit to find expression in his speech. "I can't understand how it happened,"

85

Mr. Phillips continued, "why even such a thing should happen. For everything there is an explanation but for people we have to start from scratch, like chickens out of an egg. Who would believe it of my son?"

Leon Sandler again found himself in the role of a "listening yingl" as he put it for his friend Mr. Phillips. To grow old, to know that one will soon be dead, and that for particularly strange reasons, much beyond his understanding, he could no more desert his friend Mr. Phillips than he could now grow a new set of teeth made Mr. Sandler more taciturn than ever.

Every day, usually in the evening, they would sit and talk. Mr. Phillips philosophizing about subjects beyond his understanding, Mr. Sandler listening, invoking the admiration of his friend. There were times (often after an intensive exploration of a problem) when Mr. Phillips would secretly say to himself: "Was there ever such a combination? On the whole block you couldn't find two such intelligent men. Men like us could change the world if the young would only give us their strength. The things we could do! Cities would be a paradise. The whole world would know us by our deeds!"

All day at work Mr. Phillips had waited for this hour when he could be alone with his friend. He had to talk to somebody who could understand him. The people at the shop were all dumbbells. Slaves. Nobody there had ever heard of Spinoza. Sometimes the college boys he took up in his elevator would say, "Spinoza, ya, I studied him at school. Whatta you want to know about the guy?" Spinoza was his God. A man he understood, not intellectually but profoundly from his heart, for he had never read Spinoza but the lectures he had heard at the Cooper Union Forum years ago had convinced him that Spinoza was a man who viewed the world as he did and such a man was to be admired and loved. And throughout the years he had won the respect of people by saying "Spinoza" while they nodded their heads, looked grave for an instant, and then moved the conversation ahead to more contemporary people. He had tried to think of Spinoza all day at work but since he had never read him there were no rewarding passages that he could recall to mind, and just for an instant he had looked deep into himself and was ashamed that he had never read the philosopher but only an instant. More urgent problems were pressing on his mind and his life was what it was. People knew him as they found him and didn't his friend Mr. Sandler, a wise and gifted but wasted personality, acknowledge his soundness, his judgment, his reality?

Mr. Sandler didn't answer his friend's comment. He waited for the next speech. The secret would come out. His friend's son had married a divorcée, worse, a girl without a penny and no family. He was in no hurry to know the secret. It couldn't change his life. The grave was waiting for him. He nodded his head as he had done so for the past fifteen years and waited for the next comment.

"Human beings! Who can explain the mystery? Why do people act like they lived in another world! Can you explain it to me? A boy with everything and what does he do?"

Mr. Sandler felt the awful burden of his years. The same old story was going to be repeated again. He didn't want to hear it, not again. He had nodded his head once too often. This time he would put an end to it. He had a few years of life remaining. He could put them to good advantage. The hours he spent sitting and listening to Mr. Phillips whine about the world could be spent sitting in the park, going to the National Theater—or what? What could he do now? Could he dance? Make love to women? Was there life left in his body? He was the Siamese twin of Mr. Phillips. He had to listen. There was no place for him to go. The world had shrunk down to this.

"I gave him everything. An education. A feeling for the world. He moves like a man, not like an East Side bum. He's no dummy. I guarantee you that he'll make more money than his father." Mr. Phillips was taking his time. The groundwork for his tragedy had to be laid on a firm foundation. He could see far enough into the future to feel that this might very well be the last event of importance to take place in his lifetime. To Mr. Phillips that was the burden of being a philosopher, to know a thing, an event, a person, for what it was, that was the price intelligence had to pay. All great men suffered. To suffer on a dignified plane was an exalting experience but to suffer because of one's son, no, that was just an ugly fact of life.

How would Mr. Sandler respond to his secret? Would the revelation awaken him to action? His friend was showing signs of decay. Life had already marked him for the grave.

Mr. Sandler began to experience a terrible desire to go into his room, sit down in his chair and just think. But he didn't have the strength to turn his desire into action. So what, so he would go into his room, he thought, what could he think about? Heroes? Millionaires? Big shots? So he didn't have $50,000 in the bank to leave to Yale University.

Mr. Phillips was searching his mind for words to phrase his bombshell. He wanted the words to explode in his friend's mind. The world could no longer be the same after he made his statement. From that moment on all things would have to be viewed in a different light. Mr. Phillips was thinking of the Yiddish plays he had seen on Second Avenue. In the third act with all the characters on stage there came the revelation and after the revelation everybody's life had changed. It was not the same old world. Something had been added or taken out of the world. That was the effect Mr. Phillips was searching for.

Mr. Sandler waited. His head nodded just a little. After all, he was an old man. How long could he sit on the stoop on a hot summer night without feeling a little drowsy?

Mr. Phillips sucked in his breath, a habit he had picked up years ago to permit himself time to think before answering a question. He could not find the words to tell of his son's actions. But neither could he hold in his secret any longer.

"My Joey is going to have a baby!"

Mr. Sandler sat up straight. Joey with a baby! And no wedding license. No wonder. So this was the great tragedy. But it could be straightened out. A simple ceremony.

"He won't marry the girl," Mr. Phillips continued. "She's going to bring him to court."

"By why won't he marry the girl?" asked Mr. Sandler.

"He says she's no good."

"Mr. Phillips, what will the people say?"

"The people? What people?"

"The people on the block."

"What do I care about the people on the block. For me this is a very personal problem."

"But the people listened to you talk about Spinoza. The people see in you a man who has devoted his life to justice, truth. To being a moral man. Haven't they looked upon you as a *macher* on Spinoza all of these years? What will they think now?"

"Who cares what they think! My Joey is going to have a baby. The girl is going to take him to court. This is no time for philosophy."

"But all of life is philosophy. What we do and say, that's our philosophy. And if your Joey is going to have a baby and he won't marry the girl then that is an evil thing. And your reputation will suffer. People have a short memory—"

"You mean—" Mr. Phillips stopped himself. He saw what was happening. Mr. Sandler had never liked his boy. A goof he once called him. So he was glad that Joey was in this pickle. You can't trust anybody, he began to tell himself. We're all alone. In the whole big *verstunkene* world we're all alone. Nobody cares a nickel's worth whether we live or die. Who knows? Maybe his friend Mr. Sandler hated him more than anybody else on earth. What a tragedy life was. "Tell the truth," he said, unable to contain himself, "you wanted to see my Joey in this pickle!"

The challenge was almost too much to refuse. But Mr. Sandler held off. It was too late now in life to unbind old hurts. His friend Mr. Phillips had to express his anger to someone: wasn't he miserably afraid of his own son? It would be better to sit and nod his head and let the remark pass as hundreds of such remarks had been forgotten in the past years. Maybe, when they were both dead they would find themselves in a happier world where they could sit and talk without the terrible fear that they were always in the danger of exposing something unmentionable that seemed to lie like a coiled snake somewhere deep down in their poor bodies.

When my friend Abe finished the story I asked him, "What do you think?"

"It's not life," he said.

"Not life—what the hell do you mean?"

"It's not about people—it's about an idea."

"Maybe you'd like the story better if I described how they sat down on the toilet or picked their noses or used to lay on top of their wives."

"That still wouldn't be life."

"Look you—" I started to say. But I caught myself. We had gone over this ground too many times. I knew how he used to sit in his room on Upper Broadway for hours trying to "write." And I knew how sick to my stomach he always made me feel when he'd get to talking about the long serious novel he was going to write some day, not like the crap being turned out today. He had lived a full life and he could write a full book. The *pisher!* But why get into an argument? He was good company. And why argue over a story? It was just another piece of fiction, wasn't it?

The Island

IN THE DAYS BEFORE I BECAME OLD ENOUGH TO DO
what I wanted to do, my whole family would sit in the kitchen on
cold winter nights and talk to one another, that free, insightful talk
which is only understood among families, and then only when the
moment is ripe, and that usually meant talk about money or brief
glimpses into the future which made everyone just a little bit afraid
that they would be alone and so the talk had a warmness. If there
was a shortage of coal the radiators in the dining room and living
room would be turned off, the connecting doors closed and the oven
door would be wide open, the heavy gas heat hanging in the kitchen.
My mother would sometimes talk about her boat ride. And my
father would make his rare personal statements about how he once
peddled in New York and of the streets he knew east of Third Avenue
—and if the air hung heavy enough he would go further and further
into the past and talk about his ocean ride. And sometimes our
neighbor's son would come down from upstairs, a merchant marine
sailor. He had actually been to China! He would pick me up under
the arms and set me on the kitchen table and talk about the Atlantic,
the Pacific. And the whole family would wonder how he found himself in China and sometimes Japan and even the South Sea Islands.

I looked for the ocean when I first came to New York. I found that
Manhattan was a real island—and that it only cost a nickel to sail

out into the sea. The Staten Island ferry sails out into the bay, past the big freighters, the Statue of Liberty, you can even take two or three turns around the deck before the boat docks at St. George. Hot coffee is served, grilled frankfurters. Couples hug the railing, smiling into a camera. The sea gulls wait for the popcorn boxes. If you stand on the lower deck you can feel the boat driving through the water, the waves rush up to swamp the parked cars. But if you stand on the top deck, as most people do, behind the iron guard railing, you can see the buildings telescope one into the other, the tallest buildings catching the sunlight, and then as the boat pulls out, the upward sticking mass of brick rising toward an impossible sky of white billowing clouds. The whole city stands massed, nailed to rock, screaming like some Prometheus for deliverance, though on the water you can't hear the screams that you know are everywhere.

Water encircles New York. You're never more than a dozen blocks from the water. At night, no matter where you live, a basement flat, a terrace duplex, Lexington Avenue, upper Broadway, West 10th Street, you can hear the ships signaling to one another. If you stand under the West Side Highway at Cortlandt Street you can look up and read the names of distant ports: Antwerp, Lobito, Port Sudan, Genoa, Karachi, Bombay. It's only a 10¢ ride on the 49th Street cross-town bus to the West Side docks to see the boats of the U.S. Lines, the Cunard Line, the French Line. Here, the travel ads in the Sunday *Times* come to life, baggage packed, people actually sailing to Europe. And under the docks, sleeping in doorways, on the pavement, propped up drunk, wandering, poking in and out of rubbish cans, empty wine bottles making a neat pile, muttering, building fires in the winter, the merchant marine men who can't go to sea any more walk out their days. Some sit in the small cement park opposite the Seamen's Church Institute on Coenties Slip and spend the day on the benches waiting for a ship to come and carry them off. "To hell with the mountains," the man in oversized blue pants, wearing a soiled denim shirt, his face newly shaved, nicked, bleeding, his feet cased in sea boots, tells you. "I can peel potatoes, carrots, peas, but the bastards will only pay you a hundred a month. On the sea I can make three, four hundred." And then he points to an official building. "The son of a bitches won't give me my seaman's papers until one o'clock. I've got to wait until one o'clock. And then I can go anywhere in the goddamn world. At one o'clock I can pick up my papers." The ship's bells at the Seamen's Institute strike 11:30. "Summertime, there's no reason for me to be on the beach. I'll get the hell out of this son-of-a-bitching phoney town. But you can't leave with nothing—you've got to have credentials."

The Seamen's Church Institute across the street is a huge hostel with a beautiful chapel and big comfortable chairs in the lobby where merchant seamen sit all day between ships and spit tobacco juice. The room rates are reasonable and the shipping companies are just around the corner at the tip of Broadway. Messages are posted from ailing seamen on a bulletin board asking their friends to come and see them at the U.S. Marine Hospital on Ellis Island. Everybody seems to be a stranger. Beer and whisky make you less of a stranger. The South Street bars facing the East River docks a block away from the Institute would disappoint a Hollywood director looking for the *real* thing. Barmaids serve drinks instead of hairy-armed bartenders. The men drink quietly until they flop face down at the bar or on a table top. All along the waterfront, the length of the West Side docks, you see only a few of the tough, mulling bars.

At the National Maritime Union hiring hall on West 17th Street off Ninth Avenue, you can see the men waiting to ship out. A lot of foreign accents are heard. The hall is crowded with men, some standing in a great square, others sitting on straight-backed chairs. A big slate board lists the names of available ships, the port. An announcer behind a microphone calls out the job listings. "Wiper." The men look up. The ship is rated old, the lowest grade. The men know what to expect on an eighteen-day haul. But there's always a man for the job. Your shipping papers must be in order. The unions have cleaned up a lot of the sea, the men even get vacation pay now. But the sea itself is beyond reach. "You sail on a tanker down to Texas. Slow. The goddamn boat moves slow. What the hell happens when you get to Texas? Nothing. I wouldn't even drink in those miserable Texan bars."

The bars in Greenwich Village are filled with merchant seamen who'd like to be painters and writers; writers and painters who'd like to go to sea. A seaman with a Vandyck beard, a corduroy jacket, army suntan pants, brings four beers to a table. The girl who can't keep her breasts from spilling over the edge of her dress takes a beer. A seaman in a blue tropical suit walks over to the table. "Are you a painter, a writer, a sculptor or a musician?" she asks on the strength of four beers. "OS," he says. "Ordinary Seaman," she laughs. "You think I'm ignorant," a square-faced seaman who talks through closed lips tells you one night. "You think I'm ignorant because I go to sea." I never said anything about you being ignorant. "I can talk philosophy better than O'Neill can write it. Bergson. You'd have to look inside of a goddamn beer bottle to find anybody in the Village who really read Bergson." What about Bergson, you ask with a flush, trying to remember what you read. "To hell with Bergson. He's just a name. You read books aboard a ship, don't let yourself be fooled. Plenty of guys mope, piss and mope. On the last trip I read the *Vicar of Wakefield* for the first time." Wacker lurches at the bar of the White Horse, his red wine spilling. "Where can you sail to?" he asks like a Mahler baritone. Honduras, you say, Sid writes that the temperature is always 72. "The hell with Honduras. If it was any good somebody would have found it already. Nobody goes to Honduras. Twenty-three days to Denmark on a coal boat." You always wanted to go to Denmark, you tell Wacker. "You get to Denmark. So what? You get off the boat. The crew has three days. What can you do but get drunk, maybe get screwed a couple of times. Denmark itself, maybe it's beautiful, maybe it isn't. But you keep thinking, New York, New York, that's where you have to make your stand. You get off the boat in New York. The Christopher Street cross-town bus is waiting there. The Federal Building is still painted red. The same bus. The same streets. The same goddamn bars. The same people. Twenty-three days to Denmark and nothing has changed." The painters and seamen mix. It's difficult for a painter to get up rounds of beer, it's equally difficult for a seaman to find the kind of talk he'll get in a MacDougal Street bar. The seamen are free with their money. And the painters seldom go to sea. Maybe once or twice, to sail a tanker to Florida, if you have enough discipline, to see what Europe is like.

Not all people can go to sea. You can tell the Fulton Street Fish Market by the old retiring ladies who come to the pier off Fulton Street to paint the big buildings, the Brooklyn Bridge, the tugboats, the few remaining fishing boats that sail directly into the New York fish market. The boats have real canvas sails, ladders of knotted rope. "A load of scallops. We catch them and sell them." The Norwegian fisherman tells you about the boat when you point to the canvas sails and ask him if they're real. "Sure," he laughs. "But we don't use them to sail. Mostly to steady the boat." You have to be a sailor to work aboard a fishing boat. The guardrail isn't more than two or three feet high. "A storm came up in the Atlantic. I thought we were all dead. The storm made me half-dead. A big wave pushed me down and cracked my head open. Now I can't talk so good. I know the words—but to say them, just the way I see them, that I can't do so good yet on account of the accident." It's hard to sail in a little boat like yours. "Hard. Yes. But I have a house in Jersey." The drifting men have discovered the Fulton Street pier. The big trailer-trucks park at the edge of the pier. The men come to sleep under the shade of the trucks, cooled by the open breezes of the East River. The fish market is high glory. Here men work like the sculptured figures you see in post-office murals. The men wear army fatigue clothes, dungarees, a thick belt with an ax-hammer, a big iron hook hanging from the belt. The ax is used to rip open the crates of fish, to hammer the crates together for shipment once the crushed ice has been shoveled in. The hook simplifies lifting the crates. The market opens at 6 a.m. and by the afternoon the fish have been carted off to the Third Avenue restaurants. The men work swiftly to sweep up the dead fish from the gutter, to wash away the odors.

The clerks from the lower end of Wall Street come down to the pier at the foot of the street during their lunch hour to eat their packed sandwiches, to stare at the Coast Guard launches, sleek modern boats, run by coast guardsmen in faded denims. The office workers follow every movement as the exhaust fumes stir up the

East River. The boats are free to patrol the port of New York, the sea is beyond. From out of the big buildings on Broad Street, upper Wall, Broadway, the government workers, the clerks, secretaries, executives, cross busy Broadway at noon and hurry over to Battery Park. The Park is at the very tip of New York running in a graceful sweep to Pier No. 1. The entire bay is visible. Governors Island, Bedloe Island, Ellis Island, the nearby Jersey shore. But more important to the thousands of New Yorkers who gather at noontime in the newly completed park is the water. The Atlantic Ocean is only two or three feet away. You can lean against the iron railing for the better part of your lunch hour and stare at the swirling water. The water of the bay is rough, rising swirls, whitecaps. The executives bring their little grandsons, boys dressed in cord suits. And why not? Here you can see New York harbor. No looking down from a penthouse terrace, or out of an office window, the fixed-up roof of a six-story tenement. The water is right next to you. The executive and his grandson hurl rocks at the floating debris, waiting for the Statue of Liberty boat to dock.

Flocks of children come accompanied by their parents, some to ride out to the Statue, others just to sit and stare at the ocean liners that sail by. The port is always busy. Tugboats, police boats, freighters, railroad cars being floated. The wise people read the boat schedules posted in the *Times* and *Tribune*. The *Ile de France* sails into New York at noon. The *Queen Mary* leaves Pier 90 at 11 a.m., passing the Battery at 12:00. Thousands of New Yorkers lined up in the rain to see the *United States* make her entry. Boom, boom, boom, went the foghorns of the *United States*, the tug-boats nestled broadside kept silent, then at the entrance to the Hudson River, all the boats tugged at their whistles and horns. The man next to me holding a black umbrella said, "It's something. Something. There's nothing like it. Nothing like the sea." The office workers get philosophical under the steady swish of the water. Three young men in rayon summer suits with bright bow ties stand and stare. "I know myself how I picked up a lot of distorted notions. It's a shame. Millions of people are ignorant. They just don't know anything.

Take my wife. When we got married I told her that we had to take a blood test. Blood test—she thought I had syphilis. Her and her whole family. And I married her." "But Al, then there's the trouble you can teach people too much—" "Now you're getting old-fashioned." "How much is there to know, tell me just what does a person have to know to live in this world?" "What I want to know, is how do you get to ride on that thing?" and he points to the *Ile de France*.

If you can't sail the Atlantic the next best thing is to contribute 50¢ to the Seamen's Welfare Committee and board one of the ocean liners between 44th Street and 52nd Street on the West Side docks. A band plays marches. Flags wave. The first-class passenger lists are posted and you can look for the movie stars. Men stand at attention in white uniforms, obviously anxious to cater to your whims. It's visiting time before the liner heads down the Hudson for Europe. The decks are filled with aged couples posing in front of loading booms, against the railing, waving to the stationary New York skyline. A group of nuns pose in a group, smiling, the priest looks stoically into the camera, remembering to smile just before the click. Here come the college girls! Big bones, lanky bodies, Midwest, Deep South accents. American girls in neatly tailored dresses, makeup in order, cigarettes going. One girl tries to live up to the ads by appearing at two-thirty in the afternoon in a low-cut, breast-revealing, black, off-the-shoulder dress. Why doesn't one of her friends tell her that she looks like a ship's whore?

The dining room lives up to the ads, to the dream. The visitors and passengers gasp as they walk on the soft carpeting, past the intimate tables, the bandstand. "It's beautiful, beautiful, mother, this is where we eat, isn't it?" "Yes, dear, first class." The lounge is as breathtaking as a Statler lobby. Soft chairs, deep couches, all arranged in neat geometrical patterns, immediately satisfying. The stewards are all freshly shaven. They hurry down the ship's corridors with trays of *hors d'oeuvres*, champagne glasses, buckets of ice. The stateroom doors are wide open on the first-class deck. Bottles of Scotch line the bureaus, and only the best bourbon. Champagne is cooled off in tall buckets. Parties go on in almost every stateroom.

People stand sipping their drinks, crowding the corridor. "I want to thank my partners for making this trip possible!" A lot of laughter and more whisky is poured. Everybody seems to be doing it up right. The cocktail lounge is roped off into sections and men in tropical suits stand drinking whisky highballs. The waiters stand at stiff attention behind bottles of Scotch. On a lower deck a man with an accordion insists on playing "Roll Out The Barrel" over and over again. The big parties have trays and trays of *hors d'oeuvres*, chocolate cake for the youngsters. America is sailing to Europe and champagne is part of the dream. A teen-age girl balances a glass of champagne. "I'd love to make the trip," she tells her cousins. "If you work hard and save your money for ten years, then you can make the trip," her uncle tells her. "Oh no," the girl insists, "I'm going to get married and my husband will take me." "Ho," his wife laughs, "that's what I thought!" On the top part of the lounge six people sit around a table loaded down with canapés, champagne and Scotch. A middle-aged woman sits dangling a glass of champagne. "Steward," she says to the man in white standing at rigid attention, "you've sailed this line before?" "Yes, madam." "You'll take good care of us." "Oh yes, madam." A friend in a cord suit enters the roped-off party. "Champagne, darling?" she asks. Nothing to drink, he shakes his head. The steward bows. "Champagne, sir," he asks, "Scotch?" "A little Scotch." "Good, Scotch is the drink." The liner seems to be overflowing with whisky. But no one seems to be really high, drunk. Just one man carrying a bag full of empty beer bottles who insists that the band play "My Wild Irish Rose."

The people who aren't concerned with sipping champagne want to see the swimming pool. No one can really believe that the liner has a swimming pool. On all of the decks people hurry down the gangways toward the swimming pool. Where are the movie stars, the ambassadors, the tennis champions? "I remember when I came to America. Music was playing when you got on and off the boat." The champagne is for the people who remember the formula from novels, the movies. But many people simply sit in their cabins, waiting for the liner to sail. What they want to see is on the other side of the Atlantic, old friends, relatives, the place where they were born. "Look mother, a ping-pong table!" You didn't expect to see so many children sailing to Europe. "Ben," you hear a fellow say good-bye as though he's rehearsing a role for a Broadway show, "wonderful trip, all the best, I'd love to follow you—" and he drops his hand down toward his waist in the direction of his pocket which probably means he can't afford the fare. The luggage is all aboard. The deck hands seal the hatch. You have to get off the boat, hurry down the gangway. Boom, boom, goes the foghorn. The pier is lined with people taking snapshots of the liner. Pitchmen hustle orchids, picture-postcards. You can buy a frankfurter with sauerkraut and a warm bottle of soda. The porters are busy counting their tips. The tugboats nestle in. A blast from the liner and the tugs nose the liner out into the mainstream of the Hudson. "She's going to Europe?" a gray-haired man in a blue tropical asks. To Europe, you say. "Europe is there," and he points his hand toward Staten Island. Then he nods his head. "It's a miracle the way the boat can stay just on top of the water and sail and sail and get to where it's going. It must be smart men who run the boat."

The working docks from Battery Place up the river end at 72nd Street where Riverside Drive claims the Hudson. At 79th Street the yachts are anchored. Real yachts, just as real as the long line of penthouses that look down on the Hudson from the Drive. You stand and watch an attendant pump gasoline into a cruiser, 437 gallons for a total of $70.00. Running a big cabin cruiser is just as expensive as giving cocktail parties. At 11:00 in the morning the open deck of a boat is crowded with invited guests sipping either iced tea or whisky highballs. Two boys home from military school sit up stiffly in their deck chairs, respectfully answering all questions. The owner wears an Abercrombie & Fitch admiral's cap. More than two dozen motorboats sway at the yacht basin waiting to put-put up the Hudson. Two lean men in gray flannel jackets, army suntan pants, climb aboard their boat. "Where to?" one asks. "I don't know," his friend answers. "Up the Hudson. The Seine, the Thames. The Hudson is a goddamn river." Dead fish float against the side of the boats, probably killed by the gasoline fumes.

The Riverside Drive dwellers who can't afford yachts buy foam rubber sport shoes, corduroy jackets, trilby hats, and stroll along the bank of the Hudson inhaling the river air. The long promenade looks like a ship's deck. The city planners wisely used wooden railings colored by the sun and rain to line the breakwater. A French governess wheels two little girls, speaking to them in French, getting back an accurate accent. The businessmen, the professionals, from out of the long line of apartment houses, drop their New York *Times* on the park benches and take constitutionals, walking the length of the Hudson with a steady step. Couples hug the wooden railing that won't let you forget an ocean liner and watch the drifting flotsam, stare at the yachts nosing out of the basin into the Hudson. Across the Hudson is Jersey. An enormous television tower almost as tall as the Eiffel sticks up into the clear air of Jersey. The new world rising on the cliffs of Jersey is visible, red-brick projects giving their tenants a smug view of Manhattan. The bank of the Hudson is accessible for almost the entire length of its New York shore. Tennis courts, handball courts, baseball diamonds, green grass, lovers' lanes for parked cars, the misty primal view beyond the George Washington Bridge, line the river. And the river isn't ignored, the people come to stare at the water, even though, for the most part, they have to climb down from the stiff heights of Riverside Drive.

The East River, strangely enough, has no yachts, only castles built on the edge of the water. Beekman Place and Sutton Place hang over the East River. Enormous picture windows give the tenants a clear view of the tugboats, the freighters that seem to be lost as they steam up toward the Harlem River. The East 50's apartments form a solid chunk of luxury. Even the old three-story walk-ups have been painted, renovated with picture windows. A steel footbridge extends out from Beekman Place to give the people from the East Side tenements an opportunity to gaze on the water, feel the breeze. For this is the neighborhood of "Dead End." Two docks still stand under the shadow of the UN Building where boys dive into the East River to cool off from the heat. Off Sutton Place, on 57th Street, a park hangs over the East River, a sandpit for little girls in hand-embroidered dresses, benches for mothers who may or may not have martinis in their thermos. "Hey, Ronald," a boy in a T-shirt with the shield of his private school calls out, "please throw the ball right." A promenade extends along the entire length of the East River except where docks and heavy industry prevent it. At 79th Street the promenade becomes van Goghish. Graceful foot bridges, beautifully turned steel work, a lighthouse on an island, Chinese trees, a lookout not unlike the forward prow of a liner. Here, the upper East Side flat-dwellers pour out at night to cool off. And too, the real estate people have erected towering blocks of terraced, balconied buildings, a view for every tenant. People actually use their terraces. A freighter blows its warning signal. A terrace door opens and three people come out in bathrobes to watch its passage around the curve. Immediately on the river is high luxury. But two blocks away is First Avenue, Second Avenue, Third Avenue, rows and rows of railroad flats. No breeze can get through the cement. In the summer, the Irish and Italian families across the street from the Gracie Square brownstones, the Hungarian and German families from Third Avenue, Yorkville, come to the water and turn their faces into the cool breeze. The East River always has movement on it, freighters, tugboats, sight-seeing excursion boats. But the water itself has a movement that seems to be tied up with the unending breathing of a person and the mystery of it isn't lost.

But how can the water be touched? At Coney Island the Atlantic can be touched, the water scooped up, the body turned backward into the surf. Old women lift their cotton dresses and wade into the salt water ankle-deep. The surf pours in. A million Sunday bathers lie stretched out on the sand. The surf is gentle. The ocean liners pass Coney Island on their way to Europe. The 250-foot parachute jump tower must be a landmark at sea. On the beach are ten thousands of the people who made the early crossing to the United States. They come on Sunday with baskets of food, the Sunday newspapers, sun lotion, sun glasses, fishing rods, hooks, bait, portable radios, the urge to plunge into the salt water of the vast Atlantic. One woman with her legs wrapped tightly in orthopedic stockings dips her feet in the ocean. The little babies stretch out on the sand and let the surf swamp their bodies. Hot dogs on paper trays are carried from the boardwalk. Hundreds of rubbish cans line the beach. The sand stretches for miles, washed clean, bright, by the ocean, winding along the Atlantic, past Brighton Beach, Jacob Riis Park, the Rockaways, finally to Jones Beach, the far reaches of Fire Island. At Coney Island and Brighton Beach, vast apartment houses line the streets. Families live all-year-round within sound of the surf. From the roof of the six-story flats, the expanse of the Atlantic can be seen. At night when the families head for home, to walk through the hawking lights of Stillwell Avenue where girls still dance the honored "hootchie kootch," past the boiling ears of corn, frankfurters, watermelon, hot knishes, pizza pies, French fried potatoes, chow mein sandwiches, the roller coaster roaring, the ferris wheel safely rocking, down the still side streets to their four-room Brooklyn flats, the IRT, BMT subways, the surf fishermen come out, the dating couples who wrap themselves tightly in blankets, the families whose windows aren't blessed with cross ventilation.

The yachts may dock at 79th Street. But at City Island, which is curiously a remnant of New York, a finger of land breaking the water of the Atlantic, *hundreds* of boats are docked, weekend sailing captains exploring the sea. As the bridge over the bay is crossed, the boats come into view, certainly one of the most spectacular sights in all New York. As far as the eye can see, cabin cruisers, powerboats, rowboats, ketches, sails unfurled, sway in the water. Fishing parties sail toward the tuna. The account executive rows out to his cruiser and from Friday to Monday morning he sleeps at sea, not bothering to put out of the bay. Couples from the Bronx, whose proud possession is City Island, price the motorboats hoisted on display racks in the shops that line City Island. Two hundred, three hundred dollars, can put you out to sea. Three lights mean a tugboat hauling cargo. You learn the rules of the Atlantic by buying a boat. Al asks you to hold the sail into the wind. The wind fills the sail. The boat moves effortlessly, powered only by the turning axis of the earth. Where is Eighth Avenue and 22nd Street? The third floor walk-up? The refrigerator tucked away in a corner of the kitchenette.

The all-night burning lights of Pete's Delicatessen. The Abingdon Square bus filling the avenue with exhaust fumes. The curious smell coming up from the iron grating above the subway tunnels, that tells you you're home when you arrive back in the city. Al actually steers by a star. It's beautiful and lonely. Do fish ever sleep? No, Al says, fish never sleep.

The Roof

Mrs. PHILLIPS WALKED DOWN PINEAPPLE STREET PAST old Dutch houses, red-brick and shutter-windowed, skylights changing third floors into studios, white organdy curtains hanging, wing chairs resting on hooked rugs. The names of the streets, Pineapple Street, Orange Street, Cranberry Street, Willow Street, made the whole Brooklyn neighborhood seem like a watering resort. Quiet, peaceful streets like rooms in a museum, not like the wild, wild turning of faces in the hotel lobby. Mrs. Phillips turned off Pineapple Street into the Promenade and the clear blue water of the bay. Look now on the Promenade, her eyes told her. The English baby carriages. How happy and sad all babies look. The old men in white sneakers and linen jackets, bones chilled by the warm west wind from Jersey. The New York *Times* turned to marine intelligence, pencils checking arrivals and departures, boats moving across the Atlantic to Liverpool, Le Havre, Rotterdam. Women in musty silk prints sitting under the juniper trees talking above the wind in old New York accents. And she remembered once, thinking how strange it was she should have remembered the whole speech, overhearing a woman saying, a woman with an old fur collar around her neck, "And I said, I said to my friend, Susan, you know her, she's the registered nurse who comes out every night and only sits on the Montague side, well, I said to her, Susan, you just can't sit in your room all day long and simply do nothing, why, when you can walk down to Abraham & Straus or just sit on the Promenade, and no, she says to me, I won't sit in the sun, and I wouldn't say it to her but do you know what I think?—I think she's afraid of a stroke, that's it, a stroke from the sun and falling dead on the Promenade and having no one in the whole world knowing who her dead body is."

Mrs. Phillips walked past the empty early-morning benches as far as Remsen Street, and there under the shelter of a leafy tree and in the shadow of the mansions now converted into one-room apartments she found a bench to her liking. Remsen Street was the highest point on the Promenade and from the bench you could see the ocean liners leaving the river and entering the bay and then sailing out alone into the Atlantic. There was no one sitting near her. She folded her arms and felt the good softness of her stomach. She knew she was falling asleep when she closed her eyes in the soft breeze. A foghorn sounded far away. A little tugboat pulled an ocean-going freighter, steering it toward the open sea. And now she knew she was asleep because she could see herself figuring the money Ben had left, wondering how long it would keep her alive. The notes and pieces of paper Mrs. Barry's son had handed her. His quiet voice saying, "Don't worry, Mrs. Phillips, there's enough. Ben saw to it. The money is well invested. You just have to present yourself at the bank and they'll take care of you. Ben knew you don't live in this world without money."

You don't live in this world without money! Oh, how she knew it. All kinds of pensions, war pensions, old age pensions, widow's pensions, loans, checks from the children, relief, property, stocks, bonds, investments, and sometimes, like when her only sister Doris' husband was killed and the men in the office gave her part of their pay, but the money had to come. It kept the women alive on her hotel floor. Oh how they talked about money! At night on the roof, on the ladies' floor, behind the doors. Didn't women her age scrub floors? Bend wrinkled over heavy baskets of pretzels on 14th Street? Beg crouched on the dirty subway steps. And some ironed shirts. Or sat on chairs on hot summer nights outside their steaming East Side railroad flats with just enough of a relief check to keep alive.

And didn't she see them standing in line waiting for old clothes from the mission place. The money had to come. Ben had left the two buildings in the West Fifties that still brought in rent. The trucking business he sold when Dr. Brody told him, "Quit now, Ben, take a boat to China, rest your feet." Ben died suddenly, worn out, because all his life he had worked like a man pulling a whale from the bottom of the ocean.

The afternoon passed picking pieces out of her life, sleeping, dozing, watching little pink-jacketed babies learning to walk, falling, crying, laughing, running. So much for a baby to learn. To be a mother. A full belly. And then out, out into the world. All this waiting, and Mrs. Phillips looked up at the tall New York buildings bright in the sun, the green trees, the boats puffing on the water, bridges standing, all of it waiting for the first peek.

The sun grew hot during the late afternoon and the cool breeze from Jersey died. Mrs. Phillips got up from the bench to walk back to her hotel. She walked very slowly along the iron railing of the Promenade, turning off at the Clark Street exit into Columbia Heights. On Columbia new modern buildings, balconied, terraced, blue-umbrella'd, rose twelve, fifteen stories above the bay. Still, she didn't want an apartment of her own, not now, after moving from one apartment hotel to another trying to find a peaceful place to lie down in, from Washington Heights to Riverside Drive, up and down Broadway—the noise was always too much. The terrible traffic on Broadway. New York wasn't a place to sit on a park bench. But she liked this old downtown part of Brooklyn, the ocean, the boats, the red-brick houses. She couldn't go back into a kitchen, dusting, cleaning, shopping, buying radishes, cucumbers, cooking alone for one person. That was all past her. The drug store squeezed fresh orange juice and always had hot coffee. No mistake, she was becoming more and more like the ladies on the roof, she could feel it coming over her like a cloud, settling in one room, four green walls, a desk, a table lamp, a pink shower curtain, drapes dirty to the touch from the soot of the boats. Life was an elevator. When would she begin to rouge her face? Sit all morning in a beauty parlor? Dress up to sit on the roof in the evening as though every night was

New Year's Eve? It was that way with people, she decided. You live as your neighbor lives. And everybody forgets who made the first rules.

The elevator operator said, "Hello, Mrs. Phillips," with a smile that she liked, and dropped her off on the ladies floor. Mrs. Phillips took off her loose cotton dress and folded it over the straight-backed chair the hotel provided. She had forgotten to lower the window shade and now the room was hot and sticky. She opened the window, but there was no breeze, the wind had died. The best thing, she decided, would be to lie down on the bed and forget it was hot. She thought for a minute of going up to the roof, but then she would have nothing left with which to face the night. The sun and the long walk had made her very tired. Mrs. Phillips lay still, not thinking, seeing no pictures, tired, closing her eyes, resting, gently snoring.

The wind began again, rustling the papers on the desk. Mrs. Phillips stirred. The delicious east wind made her body start with delight. She got up and showered, standing for a long time under the spray, letting the cool water wash away her tiredness. She loved the hot and cold water, the steam that formed on the medicine cabinet mirror. Coming out of the shower, wet and warm, her body red, her flesh hanging soft in tired folds, turning white as she rubbed herself dry, she liked to look in the slowly clearing full-length mirror. "Who's in the mirror?" she would ask herself. And smile. "Me? Or me?" She powdered her body and put some cologne a niece had sent on her neck and shoulders. The cologne filled the bathroom with a party smell. She went to her closet and picked out the nicest dress she owned, a black silk taffeta with white sequins, a dress she had bought when Joseph wrote he was coming in from Los Angeles. But his plans had changed. And it was now six years since she had last seen him. Was there such a thing as a son afraid to face his mother? Maybe it did happen when people grew older. A son ashamed to look at the old face of his mother. But to be ashamed of life? Mrs. Phillips slipped the silk taffeta over her head and smoothed the material down until it lay even. Her long gray hair she tied in a neat bun and stuck an amber comb in it. Once Joseph had come to the hotel she was staying at on the East Side and they had had dinner in the dining room and he hadn't talked but only looked sad, as though he wanted to run out of the dining room. Instead of walking down 72nd Street after dinner to sit on a park bench and talk, he said, "Ma, there's somebody I have to meet after supper, downtown, in the Village. I'll have to leave right away." And he had left as soon as the check was paid, making apologies. Who do people fool? she asked herself aloud, still looking into the full-length mirror. No rouge, she decided, just a little lipstick. It was time to go up to the roof.

The elevator was crowded when it stopped at her floor. Mrs. Phillips could feel her sequins shining in the crowded car. The elevator emptied at the roof. Mrs. Phillips took her time and when she stepped out on the open roof that looked out over all of New York City and the bay and the dim glow of Jersey, she stopped and gazed, and though she had seen it a hundred times, she shivered at the vastness of the towers and roofs rising up into the bright wondrous sky. The sun was a big red ball. It hung over South Ferry. Its red fire lit the tops of the skyscrapers, making them stand even higher, reaching into the purple-streaked clouds. The ferryboats puffed their smoke to Staten Island. A big oil tanker turned its way past Governors Island to the open sea. You can't give up life.

Mrs. Phillips turned to find a chair. She chose a spot between two pillars and sat back to look out over the bay again, the beginning of where New York rose mysteriously out of the water like some giant fish, a cold giant wet fish, she said to herself. Why should she say the lights and skyscrapers, the red-brick houses, were a cold giant wet fish? It was a city, Mrs. Phillips repeated to herself. A city. And people lived in it as though life was something that would last forever. Maybe the buildings. But not the people. People don't last forever. Ben died. And Morris died. Sadie died. So did Michael, David, Ames, Molly, Anna and Teddie. Who would come to her funeral at the hotel? Who was dying, she said to herself with a smile.

She turned in her chair to hear what the ladies were saying, sitting in twos and threes, their chairs pushed together. "I was down to see my lawyer and he said to me, Mrs. Charles, with your finances I wouldn't recommend a trip to San Francisco. But who ever listens to advice? I went and stayed at that hotel where you look out over the Pacific Ocean, just like here, and then I took their famous ferry boat ride, but it doesn't come within an inch of the New York ferry boat. And I told the man standing next to me that there was only one ferry boat ride in the world and that was in New York . . ." And then Mrs. Hope began talking about Chicago. And that couldn't keep Mrs. Gibbons out and she began with London and Spain. The women had lived in hotels all their lives. Schoolteachers who had never married. Business women. Hardened faces. White skins. Who could unlock the doors at night on her floor, go into all the rooms, such ladies, alone, but how alone, and ten, fifteen years remaining? The false teeth in glasses of water. The little hidden hot plates, boxes of fancy cookies. The smell of old corsets. The cologne that promised miracles.

Mrs. Phillips turned to look at the Bay again and she saw sitting at her left a gray-haired man in a short-sleeved white sport shirt. He looked at Mrs. Phillips for a minute and then he said, "You wouldn't believe it's going to rain tonight."

"Rain—" Mrs. Phillips said, not sure that he had spoken to her.

"The clouds are dulling up. That means rain."

"I hope you're not right."

The man laughed and showed his face. The lines were deep but not worried. "I made it my hobby," he explained, "to find out what happens to the weather. We look and look at the sky but never see anything. Not one person in a million can name the shape of the clouds. So one night I walked down Montague Street to the library and asked for a book on the weather."

"And now you're one person in a million," Mrs. Phillips said. He laughed. "No," he said. "One in two billion."

"Oh," Mrs. Phillips said, because she didn't understand.

"That's the number of people in the world," he said, "two billion, and this is the number I am," and he pointed to his chest.

"Oh," Mrs. Phillips said again. And then she added, "Don't you believe that people see anything when they look at the clouds, a sky like the one out there?"

"People see the clouds the same way they see into a mirror. Only themselves. But to see beyond themselves, to see a cloud for a cloud . . ."

"You can see the world by looking at a sky like this," Mrs. Phillips interrupted.

"The world," he said.

Mrs. Phillips turned toward the ladies sitting in twos and threes and she saw that Mrs. Stewart and Mrs. Gibbons had noticed that the man at her side had begun talking to her. And when they saw her look in their direction they turned away like frightened geese.

"My name is Nichols," the man introduced himself when Mrs. Phillips turned her head back.

"I'm Mrs. Phillips."

"You're right," he said, "about the sky." The sun had dropped behind Jersey and only its redness hung in the sky. A breeze began to blow from the bay, stirring dust on the roof. "But—" Mr. Nichols added, "what difference does it make what you look at in this world? It's all a mystery. Take a telephone. How does a telephone call work? Or a radio. TV. A clown dancing on the air. Hot water all the time in apartment buildings. The elevators going up and down. Look at the boats able to cross the Atlantic. Just look at the way those buildings stand up, perfect, not an inch out of line. And look at people—"

"The sun falling now," Mrs. Phillips said. "Where did it fall to?" And she smiled at Mr. Nichols just a little.

"I think it goes around the world, to light up China and Australia."

"China, Australia," Mrs. Phillips said. "Do they know now," she asked Mr. Nichols, "every single place in the world, jungles, mountains, valleys, rivers, all the little cities?"

"Every single place," he answered.

"Oh," Mrs. Phillips said.

"I came here because of this roof," Mr. Nichols volunteered. "Look—" and he pointed just beyond the Brooklyn Bridge to the dark houses clustering under the Williamsburg Bridge. "That's where my children grew up. I had my first house in Brooklyn."

"Yes," Mrs. Phillips said, and she knew he was going to tell her about his life because she had met people in all the hotels where she had lived who after the first hello had to tell you their whole life story, as though they had to prove to you that they were still alive.

"I like the roof," Mr. Nichols said, and his lips began to tremble as he spoke because now he was thinking and remembering. "I think everyone who comes to the hotel comes because of the roof. Because from here you can look down on your own life, all of New York, see the streets, the buildings—look now at the BMT going across the Williamsburg Bridge!" The lights flickered by. "This all grew up as we grew up. The big buildings there on Wall Street. The Empire State Building—look at it. The buildings, the bridges, even the sun—" and now he laughed, and added, "are our monuments." Monuments. Stones. And the roof grew old and cold as Mrs. Phillips turned away from Mr. Nichols on her left and looked again at the ladies in twos and threes drawing shawls over their shoulders. Mr. Nichols sitting next to her was speaking nice like a man who read a lot, but still he wasn't telling the truth. And the truth was, why wasn't he with his boys and girls, nieces and nephews? To be alone in a hotel . . . She shivered as a breeze caught her unawares.

"Have you been at the hotel long?" Mr. Nichols asked.

"Three years."

"I've been living here ten years."

"Oh—" Mrs. Phillips said, because she couldn't hold back how she felt. Ten years seemed so heavy with days.

"Ten years. It's not even a day. The mind is a fantastic invention. I can hold now in my head in a single second the whole history of my life. Did you ever do it?" he asked.

"Yes," Mrs. Phillips said. She looked out at the water. The sun had now gone to China and was shining on the people in Australia, as Mr. Nichols said it would. The buildings in New York were all lit, their windows shining in the dark, because the charwomen were down on their hands and knees scrubbing the floors that would be trodden on in the morning. Somebody on the roof once said that the city paid to have the buildings lit at night so that New York would look like a city of lighted mountains. The breeze grew stronger, whipping dust from the black smoke-towers above the Williamsburg Bridge.

"Your arms must be cold," Mrs. Phillips suggested, looking at Mr. Nichols' short-sleeved sport shirt.

"No, I made up my mind long ago not to complain about the coolness of the evening when I had just finished complaining about the heat of the afternoon. It makes life a monkey wrench."

A burst of lightning broke over Staten Island, an enveloping blue-white burst that lit the sky.

"I told you!" Mr. Nichols cried. "I told you!" He pointed to Staten Island, where the sky was again dark. "The clouds were muggy. And that means lightning."

"And will the rain come after the lightning?" Mrs. Phillips asked.

"Not right away. In the summertime the sky gives off its own special fireworks." A new burst lit Staten Island, followed by more flashes. "It makes the sky a terrible and wonderful place."

The people on the roof all turned toward the Island, watching the sky for more flashes. The clearness of the night gave no hint of rain. But then a definite bolt of lightning tore open the sky and the roar of the thunder drove everyone up from their chairs and running toward the elevators. But Mr. Nichols didn't move, and Mrs. Phillips remained in her chair trusting in his judgment.

"It won't rain yet," he said. And he was right. The sky was still clear. The people slowly came away from the elevators to stand and watch the lightning.

"It'll rain," Mr. Nichols insisted, "but not right now. The sky has to tear itself open once in a while. That's what happens when you have an electrical storm. Like people—look!" And a bolt as long as the sky lit the water.

Mrs. Phillips saw the bolt and it quickened her breath. The thunder cracked again, and the roof shook a little. Mrs. Phillips looked at Mr. Nichols gazing out over the whole high-up sky and she wondered if he saw the sky at night from under his blankets, looking up at the ceiling, remembering what? We're all alive together, she said to herself. The wind brought a few drops of rain but they were carried from far off, from the ocean. There was no rain above the roof.

"This is a world—" Mr. Nichols said. "Look!" And the island of Manhattan stood naked in the white light as lightning over New Jersey tore the sky open again. "In a minute we'll have the rain," he said, "and we'll go back to our rooms and stand by the window and watch the rain falling."

Mr. Nichols was right. The rain began to fall, first gently, a few scattered drops, and then a cloud burst over the roof and the rain poured down, wet and splattering. Mr. Nichols and Mrs. Phillips hurried to an elevator. The rain had probably spotted her taffeta. She felt out of breath. It was the longest time she had talked to a man in years. Once, in a dining room, Joseph had suggested that she get married again and she had left the table ashamed. The elevator button turned red now. She didn't know what to say to Mr. Nichols standing at her side. Congratulate him on his knowledge of the weather? He was an old man, as she was an old woman. But his thinking about the weather, the clouds, lightning, rain, had made the lines of his face grow more soft. He didn't have the terrible look of the salesmen who talked about the hotels in Chicago. The door of the elevator opened and the elevator man said, going down. Mr. Nichols and Mrs. Phillips got into the elevator and they stood side by side until the fifteenth floor. The door opened and Mrs. Phillips stepped out into the carpeted hallway. She waved her hand to Mr. Nichols, who stood back in the car, and he smiled back, his face almost hidden by the press of bodies. And then the elevator door closed and the car went down.

The Strudel

"ROSIE, I'M GOING TO TEACH YOU HOW TO MAKE STRU-
del," Mrs. Dworkin told her daughter-in-law, "but first we'll have a
cup of tea."

Mrs. Dworkin filled the old blackened kettle with water and
turned the automatic gas burner. A lemon she forgot to get from the
grocery store! Too late now to run out. Nobody else was home.
She and Rosie could talk for a change. It wasn't possible to talk
with the whole family home. She had noticed how Rosie always
turned a little red, made some excuse to leave the room, would go
into the kitchen, start washing the dishes, make some dessert, do
the serving. The family joked until the jokes became insults. And
Rosie, no, not her, she shouldn't be insulted. How many Yiddish
girls would have been as good as her? When there was no money,
Joey just out of law school, when being a lawyer was worse than being
a ditchdigger, she didn't complain. Rosie went out and worked, kept
a clean house, even sent Natie to *heder*. Not once did she complain.
And the strange world she was in! Cut off from her own life. The
church she grew up in. Maybe she still missed it, the lights, the
candles, the *goyish* churches were so big, so beautiful.

"I forgot to get a lemon from Bilsky's, so we'll put an apple slice
in the tea instead."

114

Rose reached for an apple and the paring knife. "With the peel or without the peel?" she asked.

"With the peel, Rosie, everything with the peel."

The steam began escaping from the copper kettle. Mrs. Dworkin turned off the fire and poured water into two large white cups. Rosie put an apple slice into each cup.

"If I had one wish, Rosie, what do you think I would wish?"

Rosie looked up from her tea cup. "But you don't have to wish for anything, Ma!" Rosie said "Ma" like a *goye*. "You've got all the money you need, four married sons, everything. . . ."

"At my age—money?"

"But—"

"And I know how Ralphie lives with his wife. And Eddie. Cats and dogs. They scream day and night. It's terrible how unhappy they are."

Rosie dunked her apple slice again. This talk about wishes gave her a start. A wish always made her think of death. When people are so far gone as death they begin to wish. No! she didn't even want to think of ma dying. The whole family would be a lot of jeering monsters without her. The fat wives, her sisters-in-law, strutting, ignorant, making a big show at the Friday night suppers, never helping with the serving, the dishes, sitting around like duchesses, reminding her of a troop of decked-out elephants.

"They're not so unhappy," Rosie tried to tell her mother-in-law. "Some people just like to quarrel."

"Unhappy or not, they'll stay together. Where else do they have to go? But that's not what I want to talk about."

Rosie took a sip of the tea. She knew that Mrs. Dworkin was waiting for her to ask about the wish, that the question would have to come from her.

"What would your one wish be?" Rosie asked, and then waited.

"I should have used a glass for the tea. It has a different taste. What do I wish for? It's not that easy." Mrs. Dworkin stirred her tea, placed a lump of sugar in her mouth. Should she say it now? Maybe it should wait for another day. But how long could she wait?

Since the first year after Joey's wedding she had wanted to ask Rosie. It was that long! Joey was a baby when he married. How the family screamed! And to be married in New Jersey away from the family for two dollars. A bastard, they all called him. She remembered how Joey said, "But, Ma, can't anybody understand, this is the girl I want to marry. What's everybody butting in for? I don't want to marry like Ralphie, like Eddie, like George. With us it's different. You'll see. It doesn't make any difference what she is now, Ma. When she lives in my house she'll live Jewish. Not that I'm so religious but that's the way I know it will be. . . ." He was out of college and so smart! The arguments went on for days. And all the time Rosie didn't say a word. It must have been terrible for her. And then one day Rosie talked up. And how she talked! She had to go into the toilet to cry. And then the house Rosie set up. Nothing on installments. They only bought what they could afford. Pictures hung from the wall. Books. Little by little they bought better furniture. Everything their own. She didn't live like a *goye*. How she cried the first time Rosie asked her, "Ma, Joey likes *tzimmes*. Tell me how you make *tzimmes*."

Mrs. Dworkin stood up. "We'll forget about my wish, Rosie. I'll show you now how to make strudel."

Rosie got up and went to the closet to get an apron.

"I don't know how to explain it, Rosie. You'll just have to watch me. Measurements I don't know."

Mrs. Dworkin began by sifting the flour. Rosie looked on, duplicating every action in her mind. An egg was broken, oil poured, salt, some water. Rosie felt sad as she watched the pair of old hands kneading the dough. The years they worked! The things they did! Who could keep account? The dough became smooth as it was kneaded over and over again. How did she first learn? In Russia probably. In some small village. Her own mother kneading the dough. Where else can you learn such things? The white flour was now a beautiful mound. And it all seemed so simple! Now the walnuts. At least she could help crack the walnuts, cut the nutmeat. And the apples. What else went into the strudel? It was so far beyond description. Like the *gefilte fish*. That she had mastered. On their fifth anniversary, Joe wanted to go to a big night club. No, we'll have dinner at home, she remembered telling him. And then his surprise, the platter of *gefilte* fish. The ceremony he made out of tasting it. And then that knowing certain smile. What was going into the strudel now? She'd better keep her eyes open.

Mrs. Dworkin broke open the walnuts. Joey used to put them between the door and ruin the woodwork. It took her a longer time now to make strudel. So much work to it. But Rosie would catch on fast. She had a good head on her. Maybe Rosie already knew what she wanted to ask her. But how can you ask a grown woman such a thing? A woman with a boy ten years old.

The dough was ready for thinning. It had to be tissue thin. Rosie watched how the dough was worked from underneath, the fingers spreading, evening, spreading still thinner. Mrs. Dworkin rested for a minute. Now the dough was down to desired thinness. You had to play with the dough like it was a baby just learning how to walk.

"Now we have to put in the filling and it's finished."

Finished! Rosie didn't even know how it had begun!

Mrs. Dworkin rolled the dough and placed it in the greased pan. "Now the fire does the rest of the work," she said. "Let's sit down and rest."

"How long will it take?"

"Soon." Ralphie would be home soon. And then Bernice. The house in an uproar. She could never say what she wanted to say to Rosie. Why was it so hard? Some words can never come out. It's just another thing that makes people so mysterious.

"What about your wish, Ma?"

Mrs. Dworkin looked up. She heard the words!

The wish.

"Rosie," she said. And Rosie trembled all over when she pronounced her name so.

"Rosie, I would like to go to one more wedding before I die." She stopped for a minute. Rosie didn't dare interrupt. "I would like to see you and my Joey married by a rabbi, under a *chupa*, hear

Joey break the glass. Do you know what it means to break the glass? It means that your marriage will last so long as it takes to make the broken pieces come together again. That's my wish."

Mrs. Dworkin didn't know what to do with her eyes. She tried looking at the oven. The stove was turned to 400 degrees. You turned a knob and knew just how hot the stove was. How wonderful everything was made. What would Rosie say? Oh! the screams when Rosie wouldn't have a ceremony performed by a rabbi. No, she said and she wouldn't change her mind. The quarrels! It wasn't the same house. But after they were married she didn't say a word. If it made Joey happy, let him be happy. It was his life. He would find out sooner or later. And did Sarah keep a kosher house? Or Bernice? No, bacon and lobsters they ate! And then Rosie became closer to her than all the others. The way she learned Yiddish. Joey gave her lessons, made up a regular book for her to study from. Just so she, Rosie, could talk to her. And the ceremony, it was forgotten like a family quarrel.

Oh, she's going to die, Rosie said to herself, a tremor passing through her. For an old woman like her to have suffered so long with a question. Why didn't she herself, Rosie, do something about it long ago? Where were her eyes? Were they kept closed by the dream that at first she couldn't get out of her mind? She remembered sleeping next to Joey the first months, frightened, cold, almost out of her mind, the same dream every night, stamped on her from birth. Angels, white, fields of white, music, God on his throne, Jesus at his side, the trumpets blowing the Resurrection! What kind of a heaven did Jewish people have? She had never been able to find out. People just don't vanish. There must be a soul. Why didn't anyone talk about a Jewish heaven?

"Ma," Rosie said, "I want to ask you a question."

"What is it, Rosie?"

"What kind of a heaven do Jewish people have?"

"Heaven . . . the heaven . . . oh . . . the heaven is on earth. In the people who love you, Rosie, who remember you, your children, their children, your husband, Joey, friends, that's the heaven, Rosie."

"But. . ."

"Who knows what else. . ."

The strudel!

They both smelled the strudel at once. Mrs. Dworkin rushed to open the oven door. Rosie grabbed some dish towels. They both pulled out the hot pan. The strudel, brown, flaked, ageless, was done.

The Street

THE FIRST TIME I SAW 42ND STREET I WALKED ITS length, eating hot dogs all the way. East of Sixth Avenue, 42nd Street is unmistakably New York. Fifty-story office buildings, Dublin pipe shops, Tudor City, Browning King, Rogers Peet, Grand Central Station; Madison Avenue tries to reduce America to a slogan. But from Eighth Avenue to Sixth Avenue, 42nd Street is the last turn in the dream world. Habitués from Oklahoma, Iowa, Detroit, Georgia, Queens, the Bronx, Brooklyn, brownstone flats, parade the two long city blocks, unable to awaken, caught up, prodded on by the murky promises of chlorophyll, still believing life is a chance you take in a gum drop machine, led by Class "B" lure, yellow sherry wine, into further ennui.

Book shops crowd 42nd Street. One wonders at the interest in literature. The shops stock recently stricken novels at bargain prices, 59¢, volumes of poetry begging for 10¢, how-to-do-its; some, reproductions of Lautrec's Paris. The racks are fronted with crowds of men assiduously examining the sexier titles; the promise of a better job by building your vocabulary ten words a day. A study of Sade is reduced from $10.00 to $2.98. Wilhelm Stekel, the psychoanalyst, is a best seller. His books have remarkably long, detailed candid case histories that excite the men who linger over the small type. Special racks are devoted to mental health titles, psychology texts, particularly those with flagrant psychoanalytic studies. The "art study" magazines offer an endless flood of breasts. The breasts pour out, the genitalia are curiously amorphous. Where do the legions of girls come from who pose for the photographs?

A deck of playing cards sells for 99¢ on 42nd Street, fifty-two different nudes in color. The latest trade is in glossy prints, realistically snapped to impress acquaintances as your girl friend, girls photographed in bedrooms, on the beach, a chair, a lawn, a patio, two, three girls together in one pose. The photographs are on display behind the cash registers or on the tables in the rear of the souvenir shops. A big red-faced man thumbs through a stack of them and selects five batches at two dollars each. Crowds of boys, men, line the table. A sign reads: IF YOU AREN'T SERIOUS, PLEASE DON'T WASTE OUR TIME. High propriety. Why are the lewd merchants always so moral? Bookstores seem to spring up faster than cafeterias on 42nd Street. All that's required is lumber for shelving and a supply of reasonably priced pornography. The real pornography sells openly for only $2.00, sturdily bound volumes with incidents of fellatio, flagellation, Lesbianism, rape, dope parties, hotel orgies. The jackets offer a bewildering assortment of breasts, a flood of bodies. The display of the breast is no accident. The men turning the pages, scanning the covers, spending hours in and out of the bookshops, seem to be searching for the warm soft breasts they had once known, or never knew, or still hope to know.

The permanent drifting population of 42nd Street stands in the glare of lights. Unlike the Bowery which has the "El" sticking up, casting lattice shadows during the day, 42nd Street is always lit up, always noisy, a barker advertising a flea circus, auctioneers crying, "Gold! Gold! 14kt! You can pound the watchband in a ball and the assay office will give you $36.00 an ounce!" Not many cast-loose women walk the Bowery. But they do frequent 42nd Street. You have a frankfurter and a chocolate soda in Grant's and next to you, a parched woman, face hollow, body thin, teeth missing, dress shapeless, blue veins showing, her eyes sad, cries, "I've been dragging in the gutter for three years. Three years with nothing happening but going down." The tieless man next to her says, "You need some self-preservation." But his voice doesn't understand her tone. "What kind of self-preservation? What're you talking about? I want to live. Just like the next person. Three hundred pounds he weighs and he has to hit me. Why? I don't understand it. What does he prove in himself by hitting me?" "You can't take him to court. You know that all the judges are a fake. Political jobs. They don't give a damn about you." "Christ," she tells him, "don't take the last bit of hope out of me. I need sympathy, help, somebody who knows I'm alive. Just to live like this, it doesn't make sense. Jesus, this is the world and we're people with life and we're supposed to live." "Yeah," he says.

Bums are on the sidewalk. Beggars, whiskied, crippled, blind, homeless. Men standing on the curbstone of 42nd Street, not knowing which way to turn. Gangs of boys studying the movie stills. The panhandlers are human, and the dime they beg is the only recognition they can get that they're still alive. After you give out enough dimes you begin to see that the men aren't interested in the money. Begging goes on all over 42nd Street. But the prostitutes are kept hidden on call in hotel rooms. You feel as though the underworld has conspired with the police to make New York the cleanest city in the Western world. Only an occasional amateur hustles Times Square. From across the river, West Virginia, the provinces. The girl stands out from the crowd, her handbag swinging low, eyes set straight ahead, walking slowly, too slowly for New York. You wonder why a cop hasn't chased her off the sidewalk. A pretty face, dirty-blonde hair, white blouse, black skirt, high-heeled shoes. She's very much alive, not between the pages of a cheap thrill novel. Yet no man on the sidewalk makes a move for her. Probably afraid of the expense, or her inexperience, not daring to sleep with anyone who would openly work Broadway. The minute she turns the corner on 42nd Street, a tall, thin, idling, seedless man in his twenties makes an approach, seeing her as a date, trying to find the right combination of words that will make her smile, accept a drink, a cigarette. The girl doesn't make it difficult. Occasionally she turns her head to acknowledge what he has said. Overhead the marquee lights advertise *Vice Raid*, *Torment*, *Radar Men From The Moon*, *The Mysterious Rider*.

"I'm on vacation," he tells the girl. She admits to working in a radio factory. "I test the tubes all day long. Wires, pliers." "That's rough work." When she nods her head, he stops and takes out a pack of cigarettes, giving her a light in the cupped hands of Humphrey Bogart. They turn the corner of 42nd Street and Eighth Avenue, talking, smoking. You expect them to go to an off Broadway-hotel. Back on the corner of 42nd Street you overhear a broad-shouldered, good-looking boy in a T-shirt say to his friend in castoff army clothes, "She went around the block with some guy on her tail. She'd better come back with some dough tonight or she's done for." The boy in the white T-shirt, who seems proud to be a pimp, smiles knowingly at his friend. A minute later the girl comes out of the crowd, alone, still walking slowly, a silent, dumb, helpless, appealing look on her face. You expect the pimp to knock her down. Instead he asks her why? The newsdealer looks on. The boy in army clothes. The Thursday night Broadway crowd stares at the girl. Two giant near-naked bodies, brilliantly lit up, look down, thousands of gallons of water pouring over a Times Square falls above Bond Clothes.

The dream world plays to crowded houses on 42nd Street. The movies stay open until 4 a.m. The price is cheap, usually 44¢, going to 65¢, sometimes 74¢ if "A" films are shown. Gangsters and cowboys provide the images. Big black automatics, trench coats, FBI badges, whisky, one-two punches, sagebrush, horses, girls who belong to one man only. The audience has long afternoons to face. Salesmen rest their feet. Straggling gangs come out of the underground subways at Times Square. "Whatta' we going to do?" the leader is asked. "Do, do, do. We go to the show, there—" and he points to the Lyric. The past is raked, revivals always come up, films the imagination begs for. *One Million B.C.* Anthropological films shot in the South Sea Islands, bare breasts, wedding orgies. It's a curious twist on the white man's burden. You seldom see women in the audience. Only rows and rows of men staring away two, three hours. Candy-butchers work the aisles selling ice cream. Dressed-up couples sometimes come to 42nd Street to sit through an old revival or, more than likely, to get away from the high prices of the on-Broadway movie houses. The Apollo shows foreign films, educating a whole generation to Jean Gabin.

What do you do when you walk out of the movie into the smell of frankfurters, frying hamburgers, root beer, newsdealers yelling whatta' you read, girls walking by who don't drop a shoulder of their negligee when you stare at them? How do you get from the movie into life, from life into the movie?

You need a girl. Or somebody. Something. A lascivious book, glossy prints, a hunting knife, a ranch shirt sold in gaudy Army and Navy stores, a silver-plated buckle, cowboy boots, a motorcycle, blue seude shoes, black draped pants. A date. A boy in a double breasted gray flannel suit, a crew haircut, innocent face, tries to pick up a girl on her way back from lunch at Child's. The girl is young, her body revealed in a tight knit suit. You forget for a minute that you're in New York as you listen to the dialogue. "Won't you tell me your name?" "Why should I tell you my name?" He walks closely beside her so that no one will think he's trying for a pickup. "I'd like to know you. And that's the way people get to know one another, by knowing their names." "I don't think it would make any difference if I told you my name." The girl has a noticeable New York accent. "We should be friends." "Why? Do you spend all your time trying to pick up girls on 42nd Street?" "No. I just happened to see you and I wanted to meet you and I just couldn't holler out 'Hey'." "No, you couldn't." "My name is Don. Now won't you tell me your name?" "Muriel." "What do you do, Muriel?" "I'm a model." "Model—I never met a New York model before. What do you model?" "Sportswear—bathing suits, play suits." "That must be interesting work. Do you live in New York?" "The Borough of Manhattan." "That's a big borough." "Why do you want to know where I live, Don?" "I'd like to take you out. Maybe we can go swimming out to Jones Beach. I've never been out with a New York model." "Oh but I don't go out with strangers, Don." "But everyone is a stranger until you get to know them. What part of Manhattan do you live in?" "The Lower East Side." "That's a pretty tough neighborhood." "Not if you know it." "What part of the Lower East Side?" "Delancey Street. Are you from New

York, Don?" "No, I'm from New Mexico. I matriculated there.
C.P.A. I'm a Certified Public Accountant." Desperately he repeats
"matriculated" over again, spelling out C.P.A. The girl has turned
into the lobby of the loft building where she works. "Good-bye,
Don," she says very politely, "it's been very nice meeting you."
The elevator is on its way down. The C.P.A. from New Mexico
doesn't know what to say. New York is too fast, too quick, too
polite. He doesn't want to let go the thread of an acquaintance he
started. New Mexico. C.P.A. Matriculated.

On Times Square a voice cries out, "This is really Times Square!"
The real Times Square. "You know, it looks exactly the way it's
supposed to. No different than the Grand Canyon or Niagara Falls.
The lights must cost a fortune!" People, people, people, fill Times
Square. And all the people are amazed that there are so many of
themselves on the sidewalk. The columnists have educated their
syndicated readers to parade Broadway, to look for characters—a
face that you wouldn't invite to Sunday brunch. "Daddy, daddy,
daddy," a little boy begs his father, "what are we going to do now?"
"Do! We're doing now. We're walking on Broadway!" The parade
doesn't end. "Once I got up in the middle of the night in my room at
the Taft, dressed, went down to Broadway just to see if there were
still people on the sidewalk. I saw them, crazy people walking around
at 4:30 in the morning."

Pokerino! Mechanical poker, roll five rubber balls onto a deck of
cards, watch the "kings" light up. A royal flush pays off twenty
coupons. Shooting galleries, one hundred furious shots from a
Thompson submachine gun for only a quarter. Amuse yourself on
Broadway. "Take home a souvenir of New York—the big town!"
Paste jewelry sparkles on Broadway, trays of earrings, scatter pins,
rhinestones. Sewing machines stitch your name on a novelty hat.
One man stands all day behind a counter winding up mechanical
toys that wag their tail on Broadway. If you stand on the corner of
42nd Street and Times Square on a clear day that cuts the ocean
haze, you can see the green trees of Central Park. Broadway isn't
very far away from home. It simply has a larger electric light bill.

Broadway begins at 42nd Street. It ends abruptly at 53rd Street.

What are you going to do when you get off Broadway? Darkness is all around. You don't dare venture off the perimeter. The light holds the crowds. New Yorkers know Broadway isn't the world. "There's a museum right up here on 86th Street. If you went out to buy all the stuff they've got in there it would cost you $60,000,000,000! There's no city like New York," the nephew tells his uncle. "Take the car—drive around. Don't walk your head off on Broadway." It's only eleven in the morning. "Where to, kids?" asks the man in horn-rimmed glasses, New York accent. "How about the Cloisters?" he suggests. The Cloisters, they all ask, what is it? "It's a place where they have a lot of expensive art, medieval stuff, religious pieces, it's something to see." It's too hot to walk around a museum, there —they point to the Paramount—*She's Working Her Way Through College*. Movie theaters light up Broadway. The admission price shocks visitors. "This is on me, Ben, don't argue," and the man's face turns a little white as he has to spend $6.00 for two couples.

The problem is to have a good time. "Daphne," the British visitor tells his daughter, "you go see if they have tickets for *Gigi*. Mother and I will wait for you in that wonderful Automat at 46th Street." A cafeteria is safe on Broadway. You can always get away with iced tea. No tipping. "All I want is just a sandwich," is repeated over and over again, as though all the Broadway restaurants charge night-club prices. Hector's is a big favorite. A table away from you three people eat cold sliced chicken sandwiches, a thick slab of cheese cake topped with cherries, a container of milk. The three don't smile or speak. The chicken is carefully chewed. The camera is carefully placed in the middle of the table. Broadway! An amplifier screams out, "Going, going, this beautiful Swiss watch, 17 fine jewels, going at $16.00 once, going at $16.00 twice—try and buy this watch on the outside for $85.00!" A Broadway jewelry auction. The auctioneer wears a neck microphone. He yells and rants like a carnival barker. "If you're from out of town we're here to serve you. This is an auction sale! A Broadway auction. We sell a hundred watches a day, sixty diamond rings. If you're from out of town a small deposit will hold your article. We'll accept traveler's checks. Buy what you like! Now who'll give me 10¢ for this sealed carton? I say it's worth $7.50 but who'll give me 10¢?" A gimmick holds the audience, sealed packages sold for only 10¢ to the outstretched hands but redeemable only after the audience has been worked through. Fake diamond watches glitter. Sterling silver is high on the wall out of reach. The shriek of the auctioneer is Broadway, brash, loud, begging. Junk is offered. It's a way of killing an hour.

You wonder who lives in the legitimate dream world until you stand on the corner of 51st Street and Seventh Avenue. The actors come to gossip. Voices rising over a Coca-Cola complain, ". . . everyone is on the rocks. You can't get a price for an act." How do you get into the dream world? "Look at Paul, he's the best goddamn dramatic tenor I know on Broadway and he can't get a job." "How do you get a job?" the girl sitting over the coffee asks. She wears a printed cotton, has a sweet, ready-to-smile face. "You go up to the Empire State Building. You climb over the rampart and jump eighty-six floors. If you can get up and walk away from the act, you're in." The girl doesn't laugh. "But if you can really sing?" she insists. "Honey, it's easier to jump off the Empire State and walk away."

What about the people who do work? The star walks onto the pavement of 44th Street. A crowd of youngsters with pads of paper wait to greet her. "Hello, dear," the star says to the boy with the box camera. "Can I take your picture again?" "Of course, dear." The star smiles, sets herself against the stage door, click, she laughs, "Just like Hollywood." Hollywood is magic. A whisper goes up 44th Street. A crowd of idling people gather. One of the little auto-graph hunters says aloud, "She makes me so nervous, just to be near her makes me nervous!" The chorus girls come out at the five-thirty Saturday matinee break. "Didn't you see me wink at you?" the dancer in her reddish blue makeup asks her little sister. "Yes, Ruthie, I saw you, I saw you on the stage." A cotton jumper, a clown's mask. The little sister and her mother try to act natural on the pavement of 44th Street. A circle gathers around another dancer, a short thin girl who wears a pony's tail. The family drove in from Pennsylvania to see the musical. "Hey, Ann, come and meet my family." Hello, the dancer professionally smiles. Where would you like to eat, is the question between shows. Cheap! Chinese dinners are suggested. Where are the invitations to the Chambord? A girl hurries out of the stage door to greet her boy friend standing at the curb. He has a T-shirt on. "Ready for sea food?" he asks. "Do we have to eat on 43rd Street again?" At night the musical on 50th Street breaks at 11:30. No top hats. No evening clothes. No cars lined up. Eight or ten men wait on the sidewalk opposite the stage door. The men wear denim, T-shirts, loafers, sport jackets. The blue jean influence has left its mark on America. It looks like a malted milk crowd. The first girl out rushes up to her boy friend, kisses him, they walk down Seventh Avenue, flats, a cotton dress. The star comes out in a double breasted blue suit, gets into a waiting taxi and turns up 50th Street.

The loneliest men who walk Broadway turn into the taxi-dance halls. The photographs advertise dozens of beautiful girls. But when you look more closely at the pictures you see that the girls aren't beautiful, that they have coarse faces, are merely awkward imitations of Broadway showgirls. Music hits the sidewalk through a sound system hookup. The admission is cheap, usually 35¢, 40¢. The barker on Broadway offers you a free introductory pass that the management immediately revokes as you get to the box office. The dance hall is large, dimly lit, bits of orange, green, blue, red. The minute you approach the girls they spring to their feet, yelling, waving, wiggling their bodies. "Hey, honey, cutie, precious, you, you over there, you sweet, darling, come here darling, you, that's right honey, you sweet, come here!" The hands reach out to grab you. The strapless dresses are pushed forward. The girls have the sensitive running fingers of a pickpocket. They know how to crawl across your lapel. "Won't you dance with me, honey? C'mon, dance with me." A band plays slow fox trots.

The girl in front of you, a little brunette in a tight-fitting evening gown, tries to shove you toward the ticket window. The price for a dance is $1.25. No, I don't feel like dancing. "When will you feel like dancing, honey, didn't you come up here to dance? C'mon I'll show you a good time," and she rolls her body, executing a bump.

No, I don't feel like dancing. "If you don't feel like dancing then we can sit down, honey." Sit down, for what? "Talk, honey," and she smiles as though Bacchanalian orgies began at eleven. Four soldiers sitting on the waiting bench poke each other, giggling at the strangeness of having to pay a girl $1.25 for a five-minute dance. One heavyset elderly man signals to a girl and they dance $10.00 worth of time away in the far dark corner of the dance floor. A young fellow sits alone, having danced $5.00 away. The girls wait at the railing of the dance floor ready to pounce, scream. Ellen once worked in a taxidance hall to keep a painter going. "You get all the creeps in the world. Guys who want to buy your pants, $15.00 a pair, not new pants but the pants you take off in the ladies room and then hand over to them. It's a fetish whorehouse, if anything. Orgasms are frequent. Sometimes a girl will help but mostly it happens by itself. If you have a shadow dance a girl can pick up an extra $10.00. The girls don't hustle openly. They don't have to. Besides, they're too conniving to make good whores. They're crazy about being strict and proper. Maybe it's the dance hall laws. The big gag is tell a guy you'll meet him at 4 a.m. Guys can't wait for you in front of the dance hall. Bouncers kick them away." It's a rough business. "But with plenty of dough in it. It's a waiting game. You dance and dance with a lot of jerks who come up by mistake but the real lonely ones, the guys gone and cut off from the world by a lot of crazy little quirks, they're the guys you wait for. One guy took me shopping on 57th Street. I picked out a gray flannel suit. You don't always say no."

You can't sit for very long without buying a ticket. A blonde walks over and lets her breasts touch your arm. "Won't you dance now, honey?" The little brunette comes back, twisting her body, rolling her hips, gesturing with her finger. "It's no fun, I'm working, you're not. Why don't you sit out a dance with a girl and get your kicks!"

On Saturday night Glen and I were walking down Broadway. Let's stop in a dance hall for a minute, there's one I want to see on Seventh Avenue. Admission was 35¢. The hall was empty except for the girls. Immediately they set up a howl clutching for us. A loud ugly howl that you found hard to believe. Beggars. "C'mon honey,

if you won't dance then let's sit down and talk," and the blonde
winked, bending over the railing. Glen bought a ticket. I walked
away to get a coke. A minute later the blonde came rushing toward
me. "Do what your friend did, honey." What's he doing? "There—"
Glen was sitting the dance out. "Be friendly, do what he did, let's
sit out a dance." The blonde led me to the ticket window. "You
pay the same thing he did." What did he pay? "Just $5.00, honey,
it's nothing." Five dollars! To talk! "He did, honey." Glen put up a
ten dollar bill and we sat down to talk. What can you talk about!
"I'm from the Bronx," the girl in the blue evening gown volunteered.
Doris. "You know, we girls get a course in psychology before we
start this job. Men like to come here to talk to us, nice men, some
from South America, business men, professional men." At five
dollars every five minutes. It's cheaper going to a psychoanalyst.
Doris laughed. "Lots of men don't like the trouble of finding themself a girl. We're right here, waiting."

A wooden railing separates you and the girl. It looks a little like
the visiting room of a penitentiary. The girls pretend an incredible
coyness. They don't stop begging. A pack of cigarettes. Coffee.
A milk shake. "Can I keep the change, honey, for the girl in the
ladies room?" They didn't stop begging, even when they could see
Glen wasn't serious, that he didn't have a lace pants fetish. Hungry
wolves on a wind-swept plain couldn't have been more desperate.
"Here's $10.00," Glen offered Doris, "take it, buy yourself some-
thing, but don't tell the house." "No, honey, I can't take a tip, I
can't risk my job for a $5.00 bill." Smart as a well-educated phono-
graph record. My blonde suggested we dance. No orchestra, just a
juke box. Her evening gown was tight fitting, no garter belt but her
breasts were encased in iron stays and everytime she pressed up you
felt steel. After a turn on the floor, she looked up for a signal.
Time up, I asked. "Why don't you stay a little while longer, honey?"
At $60.00 an hour. You need a printing press or you have to be the
loneliest guy in the world. "Men like to talk to somebody, honey.
Nobody forces you to spend your money. It's an open door."

Radio City is the daytime eastern boundary of Broadway. Nobody
quite believes Radio City when they see it for the first time. It actually

looks like the twentieth century. A plaza with green umbrellas shading the sun, waiters in white, red-trimmed jackets, a sculptured fountain pouring water. "That's some Greek god isn't it?" "Probably Zeus or Mars, one of those guys," her husband awkwardly answers. "Look how they made it gold!" The cameras come out on the promenade. You have to lie on your back to get the entire RCA Building in focus. Straight up into the sky, seventy floors, framed between a row of speciality shops, a line of waterfalls, flowers blooming. "How did they get it so perfect!" The promenade was designed for taking snapshots. The visitors feel at ease, dressed in sport shirts, loose cotton dresses. Only the New Yorkers hurry by in linen, pima, dacron, mohair, French voile, seersucker, nylon cord, eight-ounce English wool, gabardine, Italian silk. Black silhouette day dresses.

The inside of the RCA Building is murals, marble, men's shops, guides explaining the height of the ceiling, NBC's guest relations staff smiling handsomely, acting like the future executives they hope to be. The A.R.B.-polled audience pours into the building. Crowds queue for free tickets to the quiz shows, TV programs, tours of the city within a city. Guided tours are big business. "Tour 48 ready now." Thousands of visitors aren't happy to stroll through the building on their own, to enjoy the hosanna to a blueprint. Radio is still magic. TV is even greater magic. Where, the people ask, is the main control room, the switch that relays programs coast to coast? "Mother, mother, I want to go on both tours!" "But darling, you don't see anything on the second tour." "You can see the television cameras. You can see the actors!" Girls with pretty faces and carrying hat boxes hurry into the elevators. The radio announcers walk unheralded through the lobby with big custom-draped chests.

On the 65th floor the dream of New York actually comes true. The Rainbow Room. A vast circular room that only Hollywood would dare imitate. The picture windows look out on Manhattan, Queens, New Jersey, Brooklyn. You're on top of the world. No other room in the world can equal the view from the south windows, the vast Himalayan Empire State looming sixteen city blocks away above the outpouring of New York, the hulking commercial middle ending in the financial peaks fronting lower Broadway, the Statue of

Liberty visible, ocean liners treading the Hudson, the haze of the Atlantic, at dusk the millions of lights lay a carpet of twentieth-century electrically-generated magic over Manhattan. Cocktails cost only 90¢. Beer is 60¢ a bottle. Ginger ale for the non-drinkers. Family groups come up the swift elevators. Deep South, Texas, Wisconsin. Harriet showing her mother from Augusta the town. "You mean we can just ride the elevators up here?" her mother asks. "Of course, mother. This is New York. All you need is a necktie and the price of a drink."

A short elevator ride up, five floors, is the observation roof. Every few minutes a guide leads a tour to the roof's north side. Fifth Avenue, Central Park West, their penthouse terraces visible. Central Park with its green, its lakes. The haze hides Harlem, the red-brick flats. The guide lines the people against the railing and then begins her speech. "Directly in front of you is Central Park. It's two and a half miles long, a half mile wide, 860 acres in all. That bridge you see is the George Washington Bridge. Cutting it in half is the Riverside Church, and the green-topped buildings are Columbia University. To your right is Fifth Avenue, the East River, and the big white building on the river is the Cornell Medical School Hospital. Your tour ends here. You can stay on the roof as long as you like. You are now on your own."

On your own! Some people linger on the railing before heading for another tour. "How long do we stay?" the wife asks. "Didn't you hear what the girl said, we're on our own." "Oh, we're on our own?" The roof stops the ready accusations visitors are prepared to make about New York. The bigness can't be denied. The vast lump sum is right in front of you. "Just think," you hear a Southerner tell his wife, "they got all this for $24.00" The talk after the first look is about going on another tour, Chinatown. "You heard what the guide told us, we should only go to Chinatown at night." Greenwich Village, the Bowery, are mentioned with awe. "But dear, you can go up to the Empire State Building by yourself." A girl complains, "Let's go back to the hotel and take a nap." "Nap on the train. You can sleep when you get home." "Flats, heels, the balls of my feet. I don't know what to wear to keep walking." New York is a city you can only hate with love. You wonder at the lack of passion on the roof. The cameras come out. The light meters. The trick shot for the album. Proof of the visit. The view of the bigness of New York seems to be a sight only to record on a roll of 127 film. Funny, the hostility people feel toward New York. You would think the city had been created by a shifting of mountain peaks rather than by man.

A Cup of Tea

THE LITTLE GIRL STRETCHED HERSELF OUT ALONGSIDE the man and said, "Hello Mister." He said "Hello" and wondered what would happen next. The girl was dressed in an oversized tattered green hand-me-down bathing suit and you could see by the blue of her lips that she had probably been in the water all afternoon. Her thin little body was shaking and he offered her his towel. She politely took it, dried herself and said, "Thanks Mister." She then began to look at him as though she had known him for a long time. The little girl had that curious grown-up, knowing air about her that made one feel as though one were talking to an adult.

"Will you take me into the deep water? I can't swim. Will you take me into the deep water?" He got up from the hard cement and they both walked toward the pool. He jumped into the water first and then she shouted, "Hold up your hands. I'll jump into your arms!" She jumped and splashed water into his face and then climbed on his back. He carried her off into the deep water while she squealed with delight and looked around for her friends so that she could show off.

Much later, after repeated trips around the pool, she said to him, "I have to go home now Mister, are you going home?" He decided to leave the pool. It was already past 5:00.

134

"I'll meet you outside," she shouted and then disappeared into the women's dressing room.

He didn't recognize her at first when he saw her coming up to him, an old dirty cotton dress covering her body, her hair in wet streaks, her face bright and shiny. They walked along, asking questions of one another.

She was a little Irish girl named Nora Delly and she lived on the Hudson River waterfront, on Greenwich Street, a few blocks from the Carmine Street swimming pool. She lived in a four-room cold-water flat and hated it because her mother had to heat the stove for hot water and the place was always too cold or too hot.

They passed an ice-cream wagon and he treated her to an ice-cream pie. She left him on Seventh Avenue with the promise to look for him whenever she came to the pool.

All during that summer he used to meet her in the pool and take her for long rides into the deep water. She introduced him to her friends and he soon became a celebrated person at the pool. Whenever he would come to the pool, the kids would crowd around him fighting for the privilege of riding on his back into the five-feet water.

One day he decided to invite a half-dozen of them to his room for some ice cream and cookies. That was the beginning of a pattern that was to remain for a very long time. Nora enjoyed herself tremendously at these parties and played hostess for him, deciding how much each kid should eat and how long they should stay. Once a week, perhaps only once a month and sometimes on Sunday afternoon, the kids would knock on his door and come in to muss up his papers, look at his books and peck away on the typewriter. He began to hear their conversation now. What had once been innocent babble now took order and form and he could understand the logic of their ideas. They all attended parochial school and attacked Protestantism with the same bitterness that they denounced their teachers. The more he heard Nora talk and some of the others, the more he began to be nervous about himself. He saw that these kids, the oldest of them only ten, had a vocabulary of definite opinions and many of their inculcated ideas were quite opposed to his own. He became afraid of saying certain things and the buoyant feeling he had felt all summer disappeared.

His difficulty was simple enough. He was Jewish and he was afraid that one day one of them would make some remark and he would be forced to take a position, and he wasn't quite certain what he would say. And so whenever the children spoke, he listened in dread and wondered what fleeting innocent stream of conversation would suddenly turn on him and force him to take a stand. He felt that he was caught up in a humiliating situation and he often wondered how the consciousness of this idea arose in his mind. He didn't feel particularly Jewish and he saw no reason why he should be so disturbed over the possibility of an incident. He used to lie awake in the late evening and think about the pleasant afternoons at the swimming pool and the kids fighting to ride on his back and the noisy parties with ice cream and cake. He remembered how pleased he had felt when he told himself that he was giving these Irish kids a break, taking them out of their dismal cold-water flats, exposing them to kindness, to culture, to afternoons surrounded by objects they could never see in their own homes. He felt that since he had treated them kindly, taught them how to swim and peck away at a typewriter, they would forget he was Jewish and if ever a damning phrase would form itself on one of their lips, their conscience would immediately silence the insulting words and he would be free. He began to wonder how they talked among themselves and if they ever discussed him. He would have given anything to overhear some of their conversations. But then there is something mysterious about other people's conversations and we never seem to hear them. In a whole lifetime we may only overhear one or two references to ourselves—and then it comes as a rude or pleasant shock. Almost as though we were moving through a museum and then suddenly at the end of a long corridor we come face to face with our own portrait. But what could they say? Could they call him "that lousy Jew"— "that Christ-killer"—but then why would they come back and why would they sit on his chairs and watch their feet?

One day Nora said to him, "Mama asks why you don't come up and visit us. I've told her about you."

He didn't want to go to Nora's house. And he knew the reason why. If the children hadn't been able to see through him, then the mother certainly would. And then his Jewishness would be on display. But he knew that he had to go and they set the time for the next Friday evening.

The building Nora lived in was as ugly as the rest of the tenements on Greenwich Street. He knocked on the door and Mrs. Delly answered. "Come in, come in, we've been expecting you."

He sat down in an oversized chair. The room was drab, ordinary. The oil stove gave off a curious odor. The conversation began with housing. All of the time that they sat discussing the housing situation in the neighborhood, Nora sat crosslegged on the couch, looking at her friend, looking at her mother, glad that the fencing was over and her friend able to talk to her mother.

Mrs. Delly shifted her heavy body and then motioned Nora and her friend into the kitchen. The three of them sat down to a cup of tea. And then the fear hit him. The lights in the kitchen were bright. She could get a good look at him. She would see that he was Jewish. And then she would begin to say, what did you say your name was, yes, that isn't a Catholic name, is it, what kind of a name is that now? And he would be forced to say, that's a Jewish name. I'm Jewish. As though being Jewish was the most terrible fact of existence.

He couldn't control his tea cup and some of the hot water spilled on his jacket. Nora immediately fetched a towel. "That's a shame," Mrs. Delly said, "but don't worry, it won't stain." He tried to think of something to say. He felt a terrible silence. Nora came to his rescue.

"Did you see our white kitty? We keep him to kill mice. He killed three mice last week."

"Now Nora, don't be talking to your friend about mice while we're sitting and drinking our tea. What was it you said you were studying at school?"

He knew now that there was no escape for him. She had guessed that he was Jewish. The question about school was only an attempt to link his Jewishness with a particular subject. He thought of telling her that he was studying to be a radio mechanic. But he couldn't and blurted out the truth. He was studying to be a teacher. Mrs. Delly nodded her head and he could see that she was beginning to tie up her thoughts.

"It's good that you have the patience to want to study. So many people can't wait and they get themselves jobs that lead to nothing. My Tommy could have been a refrigerator mechanic instead of breaking his back on the water front."

He sipped on his tea and nodded in agreement.

"You're not a Catholic boy, are you?" she suddenly asked. "Nora has been telling me for months about a nice man that she met at the swimming pool and she thought he was Jewish. I thought I'd ask you."

He felt himself go limp. A humiliating flush that he couldn't control swept over his face. He saw Nora staring at him with a puzzled look in her eyes. And then he could feel stirring deep within him the necessity of a retort—a defense of his position phrased in the language of the long struggle for the dignity of the individual, for the brotherhood of man, for the rights of all people—a speech that would go beyond the insult he had felt at the lips of Mrs. Delly, and unite him and Mrs. Delly and Nora into one great bond.

He placed his cup of tea down on the table. "I could never drink hot tea," he said apologetically. "It always chokes up on me."

"Oh that's a pity!" said Mrs. Delly. "Why didn't you say so before? Nora fetch your friend a bottle of cold beer from the icebox. How'll that be?"

Nora walked over to the icebox in the far corner of the kitchen. She wondered why her friend had flushed so. She had never seen him so upset. Once he had raised his voice when Molly Donovan had spilled some ink on one of his books. Could it have been something that her mother had said?

The Old Woman

IT'S A SHAME FOR THE NEIGHBORS, MRS. LEVITT USED TO say when there would be a family quarrel or her youngest boy Harry would come home from work and start yelling at the top of his voice for reasons the family could never understand. In the summertime Mrs. Levitt would run from window to window shutting them tight. In the winter she sat by the kitchen stove hoping that the neighbors didn't hear too much. She dreaded the sound of the broomstick pounding on the floor above, a signal that meant Mrs. Goodman upstairs was complaining.

But what happened the other day, that wasn't a shame for the neighbors. It was her own personal shame. Her children had held her face up to a mirror. Showed her what she was. An old woman ready to die.

Her children, so grown, Ethel with breasts already of a woman with five children, Harry, putting all his money into clothes, Meyer with his little boy and the wife he hated, Sanford, coughing, sick, living like a dog, Pauline, complaining always of her husband, he doesn't make a tenth of what other men make—her children were all in the living room and she lay in her bed, sick with a cold.

Meyer was the first one to talk. "I can't take Ma in with me. There's no room in my place. Maybe someday if we find a bigger apartment . . ."

Pauline was the second one to talk. "We can't afford it. I have enough on my mind trying to live on Jack's salary . . ."

Then Ethel. "With my three babies—no, thank you!"

So they talked, her children, as though she was less than a dog in the rain.

It all came about through Harry. He had finally found a girl and asked her to marry, but the girl told him flatly, "I won't live with your mother. Married people have to live by themselves so that they can get to understand one another—start fresh . . ." So Harry announced one day to his brothers and sisters, something has to be done with Ma. It was all right for her to stay with me after Pa died. But now one of you has to take her in.

How old was Ma? She could still bake a *chalah*, prepare whitefish, make hamburger that you couldn't taste anywhere else, walk, wash her hands and face, undress herself, wipe the kitchen sink dry, sit on the porch, talk to the neighbors—and she could still reason. That was the most terrible thing. A happy sentence made her smile. Sad news made her cry.

"There's no great emergency," Harry said, when he saw his brothers and sisters getting out of hand. "I'm not getting married tomorrow morning. But you all understand. I'm not a spring chicken. Neither is Elsie. Maybe after we're settled a little while we can take Ma in. But first we're thinking of driving to California . . ." He had no intention of driving to California, but it sounded nice, such a far-off place.

"I'll tell you what," said Sanford, the sick one, spitting into his handkerchief. "I'll take Ma in for a little while when you're on your honeymoon. Maybe a little longer. Maybe some of Ma's soup is just what I need." Sanford lived away from the house, alone, in a small bachelor apartment. He wanted freedom, he said long ago, when he still felt like accomplishing miracles. So he found an apartment downtown on 10th Street, put up a couple of paintings on his chartreuse walls, and nothing ever happened. Still people thought he was a little strange.

At first having his mother was great fun for Sanford. He bought a great pot, a big frying pan. On Tuesday his mother made soup for the entire week. A pot full of cabbage borscht with a five-pound chunk of beef. On Thursday his mother made her hamburgers. The hamburgers he packed for lunch, boasting about them in the office where he worked. His job was to paint in the roses on vases that were handled by cheap retail outlets. But after three weeks his mother's cold turned worse. Whenever they sat down to eat she would begin to cough and spit up great ugly globs of phlegm. And at night she would lay in her small dark room, coughing, talking to herself, repeating over and over again that she didn't want to see a doctor.

"Ma, you've got to see a doctor," Sanford said to her one night.

"No—"

"There's nothing to be afraid of. He won't tell you that you have a cancer—"

"Shut up!"

"Ma—"

"I won't see a doctor—"

"And I can't stand the way you cough all the time!" he whined, angry and disgusted. "It makes me feel sick!"

Sick—so that's why he got up from the table all the time—made faces like a constipated baby. If she made him feel sick, better not to talk about it. Besides, she wanted her old room back at the house. Why couldn't she go back into her old room? Harry was back from his honeymoon. Was her new daughter-in-law so perfect that she couldn't use some help? Yes, Sanford would call Harry and she would go home again.

"No Sanf, no, positively no!" Harry told his older brother. "Don't even talk about it. Elsie would walk out on me in a minute if I brought Ma to live with us."

"Why? I don't understand. What's so terrible about Ma? She's getting old, that everybody knows. But she can still take care of herself. Let her have a little peace before she dies—"

"What do you mean—die! You crazy fool! Don't talk like that!" Already, swift, sudden, he had a vision of his mother dead, the house dark, the candles lit, the wooden boxes, everybody crying . . .

He liked his mother but to drive to the cemetery in that goddamn black automobile . . . He wiped his cold forehead.

"We've got to face it," Sanford said. "Ma isn't getting any younger."

"All right—all right—I'll talk to Elsie about it."

Elsie put her foot down. Mysterious Elsie who didn't seem to be like anyone else in the family.

Harry got on the phone immediately. He had to find someone in the family to take in their mother. They just couldn't leave her out on the street.

"Hello Ethel—this is Harry," came his booming voice.

"The answer is no!" said Ethel sharply.

"What do you mean, 'no'?"

"I know what you're going to ask me and the answer is *NO!* I have enough trouble on my hands with my three kids . . ."

"But Ma isn't any trouble—"

"Then why don't *you* take her in?"

"You know Elsie—"

"I don't *know* Elsie. I've only talked to her twice. She doesn't seem to have much to say to the rest of us—"

"Now Ethel—"

"Don't Ethel me! When Pa died you said you would take over the house and look after Ma. All right, do it!"

"Wait a minute," Harry said. "Ma is just as much your ma as she is my ma. You didn't come out of somebody's left ear."

He heard the phone go down with a slam. His goddamn sister! Well, that was it. Sanford, Meyer, Pauline and now Ethel. All, no, no, no, no, no! Ma would have to stay with him and Elsie until something happened. He knew she wouldn't go into a Home. If Ma just stayed in her room, Elsie wouldn't have any complaints. But Elsie was so damn busy furnishing the place. That might bring quarrels between her and Ma. Maybe not.

Harry hired a painter for fifteen dollars and did over his mother's room. Elsie put up new curtains. Harry bought a deep-nap throw rug. The chest of drawers was polished and the room sprayed for bedbugs and cockroaches. If we just make the room nice enough, he explained to Elsie, Ma'll just sit in there all day long and read or else just sit by the window like other old people.

For the first weeks she was happy in her old room. So many memories from just a chest of drawers, the closet, Sol's suit still hanging, cleaned and pressed just before he died. Harry, her youngest baby, she had in this room. And the rest, Ethel, Meyer, Pauline, Sanford, she smiled sadly, they were all made on the bed. In the beginning she used to sit by the window and look out at the trees in the backyard and watch the warm spring wind bend the top of the branches. It was hard for her to stay out of the kitchen but she knew how much Elsie wanted to make the house her home. That she understood better than anyone else in the family. The rest all thought she was a *tsatske*, but she knew, the way people know so many things, that Elsie wanted to make up for so much lost time. Elsie was one of the girls who didn't marry at nineteen, nor at twenty-three, nor at twenty-five, not even thirty, no, she always had an excuse for waiting. Now Elsie had to make up for lost time. So she watched her new daughter-in-law cook, wash windows, sweep the carpets, clean the bathroom, make Friday night supper, and never once did she interfere.

As the weather grew warmer she moved out of her room and on to the front porch where she sat alone until it was time for supper. And after supper she would go into her room and just sit there until the lights began to go out all over the house.

Mrs. Levitt would slowly undress, taking off the layers of clothing that she was in the habit of wearing. And then she would lay still, unable to sleep, and soon she could hear the bed in Harry's bedroom. Squeak, squeak, squeak—the springs would go for a few minutes and then everything would be quiet. Sometimes Harry got up to get a towel or some water from the kitchen. But usually, after the squeaks everything would be quiet. Soon she'll have a baby, she said to herself, and another baby and . . . "It's life—it's life—" she would say to herself and try to sleep.

The warm days made her restless. Harry fixed up an awning that kept out the sun. But it didn't help. She could feel the heat on the porch. People were driving away in cars. Going to the beach. It was too difficult for her to walk down the stairs or else she would have gone for walks down the shady street. There was no place for her to go, yet she felt restless. "I'm not dead yet" she would say to herself without having the slightest qualm about the fact that she soon would be actually dead.

"Harry," she said one night at supper.

Harry's soup spoon hit against his teeth. He knew what was coming next by the sound of her voice.

"Ma," he said quickly, "how about driving downtown with us Saturday and picking out a new dress. You don't get to do much just sitting on the porch—"

Elsie looked at him as though his nose had changed into a carrot.

"No, I don't want to drive downtown," his mother said.

Harry remembered the last trip to the cemetery. Just before his wedding. God, he didn't want to go through that again. It made him sick to think about dead people. Dead, finished, close the door, stop bawling. Why in the hell did she want to go to the cemetery now? Why now? People really get crazy when they get old. He wished somebody would put a bullet through his head when he got to be his mother's age. Oh this goddamn business of staying alive— swift—good-bye—

"Harry, I would like you to drive me to the cemetery—"

The words were out and he knew he would have to go ahead with it. Oh those bastard brothers and sisters of his. No, they couldn't take her in. She had to be stumped on his hands. He'd get on Meyer's ass. There was no reason why Meyer couldn't take her in. They all made more dough than him, even that nut Sanford. Goddamn it, why couldn't he have peace in the house!

Harry's hands were wet on the steering wheel. The cemetery was about fifteen miles out of New York. His mother sat beside him, not saying a word, watching the green countryside. How much room there was for people to run around in, to play in the open, to fly like birds. How nice everything looked. "And we spend our lives in five rooms," she said, half-aloud.

"What did you say, Ma?" Harry asked.

"Nothing." She always spoke in Yiddish. He always answered her in English. And they both understood one another perfectly.

He stepped down on the gas and the car leapt forward.

"Not so fast," his mother cautioned.

Harry slowed the car down. He could see ahead the road that he would have to turn down to get to the cemetery. It ran off the main highway, deliberately hid from the view of passing cars. Smart people, he thought. The smartest people in the world run the cemeteries.

He parked his car alongside a green Dodge. "I'm going to wait in the car, Ma. You know the way down to the grave. I'll come and get you later." His mother lifted her heavy bulk out of the car and started down the road that led to where her Sol was buried three years ago.

The graves were all in a cluster, but Sol's stood off away from the jumble, at a point where the cemetery almost came to an end and all one could see was the flat green countryside.

She was calm until she neared the grave and then all at once her body began shaking and she threw herself forward and down on her knees alongside the grave. The hot sun made her feel faint. She undid her jacket and sat down on the grass by the stone, rolling back and forth, gently, like she did in *shul*. And then she stood up, leaning against the stone, her voice crying out mournfully, "Sol . . . Sol . . . Sol . . . oh why did you die. Why did you die. Oh why did you die. Why did you die. Oh why did you die. Why did you die. Why did you die. Oh why did you die. Why did you die. . . ."

She stopped to put her hands to her eyes. The sun was so hot on her head.

"Sol, talk to me. Talk to me. Talk to me. Sol, Sol, Sol. Talk to me. Talk to me. Talk to me. Talk to me. Talk to me. Sol, Sol, Sol, Sol, Sol . . . why did you die. Why did you die. Why did you die. . . ." Now she rocked back and forth, gently, happy to be next to the grave of her dead husband, happy for the first time in months. Her Sol was buried under her feet. Sol was here. Just here. She could always come to him. She rocked, not feeling the heat, happy, as though this was the place she had been looking for all her life to just stop and rest and be still.

Harry thought of honking the horn but then he remembered where he was. He got out of the car and started down the path to where his father lay buried. He knew he would have to drag his mother away from the stone. For her part she could stay there day and night. What was the great attachment? They didn't seem to be too happy when his father was living. But who knows? His mother said so little that none of them in the family had any idea of what was going on in her mind. Cooking, baking, washing, scrubbing, having babies, that was her life. And now her life was over. He kicked his foot against the dirt path. Goddamn it, why did he think that!

He could see his mother now leaning against his father's stone and he could imagine what was happening. His mother was probably moaning to herself. That awful terrible moan that didn't seem to be human. That seemed to be locked up in some deep part of the body to be used only on this special occasion. Christ, how funny people were.

"All right, Ma, it's time to go. You've been here over an hour." Harry put his hands under his mother's fleshy shoulders and lifted her away from the stone. He had expected her to fight him but instead she went without a protest. The two walked back to the car, not saying a word. His mother seemed to be more rested, peaceful, less nervous.

They drove back to the house in silence.

It rained for two days following the trip to the cemetery. His mother kept to her room, seldom stirring, only coming out for a glass of tea and some hard bread. Even when the sun came out and the days were bright again, she kept to her room.

"Elsie," Harry said one night after supper to his wife. "We've got to get rid of Ma."

Elsie gave him a funny look.

"I don't want Ma in the house anymore," he said, in answer to her look. "We don't have any privacy." And then, going as far as he dared, he added, "We can't even enjoy ourselves in bed on account of her. She stays awake listening to us."

"Your mother had five babies," Elsie said. "It's no mystery to her."

"Whatta you talking about!" Harry shouted, taken back by her honesty.

"Your mother isn't any trouble to us now. Let her have a little peace."

"You were the one who didn't want her in the first place!"

"That doesn't mean people can't make mistakes."

"I don't want her in the house anymore—"

"She's your mother, Harry—"

Harry felt hot and cold. He didn't like the way the argument was going. His wife was certainly funny. Now she was saying that Ma was his mother! Why? Trying to make him feel bad. Why? Goddamn it, you never know about people!

"All right, all right—" he said hurriedly, "don't look at me as if I was such a bastard. I took Ma in in the first place, didn't I?" He stopped and took a breath. He knew she was just waiting for him to come out with what was really on his mind. How could he say *it* when it made him feel sick even to think about it?

"Do you think Ma is getting sick?" Elsie asked.

Harry gave her a look. Did she guess?

"I don't like the way Ma has been keeping to her room. It gets on my nerves."

"But you're not home all day."

"But you are," he answered. "And she'll probably begin to affect you in the same way. I don't want any quarrels—"

"I don't mind, Harry, believe me, I don't mind. She just sits in her room—looks out of the window—washes her hands—sometimes we sit and talk. What else do old people have to do?"

"All right!" Harry said, determined to have it out. This talk wasn't getting anywhere. He walked to the dark side of the room so that he wouldn't be too close to Elsie when he said what he was going to say.

Elsie stood waiting.

"I think Ma is going to die," Harry said in a low nervous voice. "I know she's going to die. And I don't want her to die in this house. I don't want her to die in this house!"

Elsie felt herself shudder. There was something going on in the room. But it was beyond her . . .

"We'll call in a doctor," Harry went on. "On his say-so we'll put Ma in a hospital. There she can have real attention. It's the best—"

"All right, all right," Elsie interrupted, as though she understood everything. "Let's not talk about it anymore tonight. We'll see tomorrow what happens."

Harry's mother refused to see the doctor he called in.

"I won't—I won't—I won't—" she repeated over and over and over. She didn't want to listen to the doctor. Whatever was wrong with her now, was wrong. The doctor couldn't change it. She just wanted to sit now in the room she and Sol had lived in, slept in, this, their room, just to sit by the window, in the chair, lay on the bed, go through the drawers, take his suit down from the hanger, brush it off, look at the picture of Sol, his hands folded together, and the other one, shaking hands with Ethel's boy when he came home from the army. A doctor she didn't need. No doctor. Could he make her young again?

Harry knew what he had to do. Why in the hell should the whole thing fall on his shoulders? He got on the phone and called his brothers and sisters over to the house.

It was the first time they had all been over to the house in a long while. But they showed no embarrassment. Ethel, Meyer, Pauline, Sanford, all filed into the bedroom and acted as though it was only last Sunday since they had seen their mother last. When they left the bedroom, Harry ushered them into the living room.

"Ma's sick—you can see that for yourself," Harry said without any preliminaries. "She won't see a doctor. And Elsie and myself are in no position to look after her now. Somebody else will have to take her in."

"Why can't you look after Ma?" Ethel started off. "You don't have any babies in the house. And Ma doesn't look like she requires too much attention."

"I said we can't and that's all there is to it."

"There's always the Old Ladies Home," Meyer volunteered.

"You know Ma won't go into a Home."

"I still think the best place for Ma is right here," Sanford said. "This is where she lived most of her life. Let her finish out her days here."

"Shut up, you damn fool!" Harry shouted at his brother. "You're always talking about people dying."

"That's the next thing on the agenda for Ma."

"Don't be so damn smart!"

"Let's not get into a fight," Pauline said, trying to be the peace-maker. "Maybe we can talk Ma into going into a Home."

"She won't listen to it," Harry said. "How many times do I have to tell you that!"

"She just has a prejudice—"

"Ma's too old for prejudices—" Elsie started to say. They all looked at her as though she was a thief. Elsie cut herself short. To think that someday she herself would be old. That someday they would all be old. God—where's the sense!

Harry took charge of the floor again. "Sanford took Ma in. I took Ma in. Now it's somebody else's turn."

None of the brothers and sisters said a word.

"We can't draw lots on something like this," Harry said, feeling in complete command. "We'll have to work it out tonight. One of you has less objections than the rest to taking in Ma. That person will look after her for a little while. Then if Ma is all right, Elsie and myself will take her back in. After all, this is the place where she lived most of her life."

"I say the best place for Ma," Ethel started again, "is a good first-class Home. We can all afford to chip in five or ten dollars or whatever it costs to put Ma in a good Home with plenty of fine attention—"

"How are you going to convince Ma to go into a Home?" Sanford asked.

"We'll tell Ma that she needs the medical attention you can get in a Home—"

"You can't fool Ma," Meyer put in, "she's never been sick a day in her life that she needed a doctor."

"That has nothing to do with it," Ethel said furiously. "None of us are in a position to look after her. We're all grown up with our own family headaches. The best place is a Home. She'll have to go there!"

"Who's going to tell her?" Sanford asked.

The door to the living room opened. The old woman stood there in her white flannel nightgown, stained with tea and raspberry jelly.

"Are you having a party?" she asked, before her astonished children.

"Yes, Ma, yes," Harry said quickly. "I closed all the doors so we wouldn't keep you awake."

"A party," she said. None of the children dared move. "I remember once at a party. A big celebration for my brother's sister's wedding. My mother said to us children. 'One mother can keep ten children but ten children can't keep one mother.' Go on with your party. I can't sleep. My chest—" She sat down on the chair Sanford made empty for her, pulling together her flannel nightgown.

Elsie hurried over to her mother-in-law's side. "It's too late for you, Ma, to stay up. Let me take you back to your room."

"Yes, it's too late," her mother-in-law said, standing up, looking very tired. "I'm too old to sleep—I'm too old to stay awake. But God made the world this way. And who are we to quarrel with God?"

Lunch

ON SATURDAY MORNING MEN OF THE CONGREGATION
gather in an abandoned loft building on Rivington Street and pray
to God. Looking upward, three, four flights, you can see the *talliths*
through the open window, the bearded faces of Eastern Europe.
Down below on the sidewalk, little boys, five, six years old, play in
front of the congregation, silk silver *yarmulkas* on their heads, talking
to one another in a free, flowing Yiddish that seems to raise their
voices to the level of philosophy. The Orthodox, the Hasidim,
hurry by in long, black frock coats. The first and second generation
fathers of the Lower East Side walk down Rivington Street past the
locked doors of the delicatessens, the kosher restaurants, to visit,
to sit in Seward Park, on their stoops, on the orange crates that line
the sidewalks, coo-cooing at the babies in the Bilt-Rite carriages who
will have to grow up on Pitt Street. Saturday is a holiday on the
Lower East Side. Lunch is the food cooked Friday afternoon. No
broiling on Saturday. The tastiest dish is beef that has been permitted
to simmer all through the night on a flame lit before sundown.

On Delancey Street the waiters prescribe the food to be eaten.
"Take a shoulder of veal, a piece of herring." Delancey Street runs
into the sweep of the Williamsburg Bridge, the landscaped tennis
courts on the East River, feeding the appetite for a five-course
kosher meal. "Only black coffee, no cream." Orchard Street is just

151

off Delancey, the one street left in New York that satisfies everyone's vision of the Lower East Side on a Sunday noon. Pushcarts, a babble of voices, stalls piled high with nylon shirts, blouses, sweaters, work pants, aprons, silks, imported woolens, tweeds, sheets, pillow cases, umbrellas, socks, sport shirts, men yelling bargains, "shirts a dollarfifty, a dollarfifty," the expected haggling over prices, the outpouring of New York, Puerto Ricans, Negroes, Chinese, whites, gypsies, shoving, crowding, legitimately tumultuous, because everyone likes a bargain. And those who intimately know the Lower East Side make their excursion down through the massed sidewalk of Orchard Street and then crowd into Ratner's on Delancey to order strawberry blintzes with sour cream.

The Lower East Side on Sunday noon feeds the people who otherwise do their eating in the tight, cramped kitchens of walk-up flats. Families wait in line at Ratner's, packing the doorway on Sunday. Blintzes are too intricate for most wives to prepare at home. The enormous menu is scanned, mushroom barley soup, cold *gefilte* fish, *pirogen*, vegetarian chopped liver, cheese cake, noodles and cheese, potato pancakes. The men come from behind the "white on white" shirt stalls to make a plate of borscht lunch. "The Giants and Dodgers, you used to be able to get up some excitement. I remember when we were kids on Attorney Street. It was a big thing who won or lost the ball game. Try and get up a baseball pool on Orchard Street, you'll die first!" "Eat your soup, Max." "The Lower East Side is a dead potato, take it from me!" "Me, I don't get a chance to see the old streets anymore. Years ago the wife and I moved up to Inwood. 1933. It was all green then. A park."

From Allen Street toward the East River, rabbinical colleges, yeshivas, cultural meeting halls, homes for the aged, synagogues, the buildings painted over and over, the stones old, stoops broken, line East Broadway, Grand Street, Rivington Street, giving way to the red-brick mass of housing projects rising slowly along the East River. Yiddish is spoken on all the streets, by the young as well as the old. In all the little delicatessens, restaurants, marble-topped tables, the glass-enclosed meat counter, salami, pastrami, corned beef, celery tonic, cherry soda, old Jewish couples, the man in his

yarmulka, his wife helping, serve potato salad, knishes, derma, meat
sandwiches—with meat that has risen to $2.85 a pound. In dairy
cafeterias the waiters bring you coffee in a glass. The gutted streets,
debris-ridden, blocks of crumbling, dark, dirty flats, may make you
want to run amuck with modern architects but the quietness of the
Lower East Side on a Saturday morning, the openly avowed belief
in the God of Abraham, the God of Isaac and the God of Jacob,
the community here and now that comes to life on Sunday, the noisy
restaurants heaped high with food that is a part of the people,
make you realize once again that life isn't made by a shower curtain,
nor a foyer 8 x 10 feet.

In the cement park on Rivington and Lewis Streets, trees growing
out of the rock, an old man takes his lunch by opening a brown
paper grocery bag. An egg salad sandwich on soft white bread. The
little brown and white dog held to the bench by a leash begs for a
piece of bread. "Here, white bread, with your teeth it should be
pumpernickel!" The little dog barks and paws at the leg of the old
man. "See, he likes me," he happily tells his friend, a thin man in
an unbuttoned vest, a long ivory cigarette holder between his lips.
"He knows you," the friend says, "it's wonderful the way dogs
know people. Tell me, how did you get the dog?" The old man chews
his egg salad sandwich and tosses the brown crust to the dog. He
points to the puppy. "He was just born. Still a baby. The dog in a
house down the street on Stanton had puppies, and I said to the
man, please, sell me one of the puppies. All right, he said, like he
was married to the dog, you can buy a puppy for $25.00. Twenty-
five! that's a lot of money. Then make it $20.00, he said. It's still a
lot of money. Then $15.00. It's still too much money for a dog that
God made. He looked at me after I said that like I was an old man
gone crazy. What do you want to spend? Five dollars, that's an
honest price. He took my $5.00, five singles." "You shouldn't have
to pay money for a dog," the man using the cigarette holder said.
"If the little dog could talk," the old man said, "I'm sure she would
agree. He, she," he laughed, "I never bothered to look!"

The frenetic trading floor of the Stock Exchange doesn't close
down for lunch. From the visitor's gallery at twelve noon you'd

expect the callboard to shut tight, the ticker tape to black out, the telephones to echo in the huge square room lit by five-story windows. The men eat in shifts, the trading doesn't end. "Look at it!" the girl up in the gallery cries out. "Are they all millionaires?" she asks her boy friend. "Not all of them." Then she asks the impossible question. "What are they doing down there, all those men?" He looks out over the trading floor littered with scraps of paper, men rushing to answer requests, the call numbers flapping. "Selling stock." "Can anybody do it?" "No, you have to be a member." "How do you become a member?" "I think by buying your way in." "Is it a good job?" "A lifetime job!"

"This way for the lecture explanation," a girl in a red and white seersucker dress calls out. The crowd follows, anxious to have the hundreds of scurrying men explained. "The men you see with the white buttons on their lapels are members of the New York Stock Exchange. The number flashing on the big callboard is the number of each individual member. When a telephone order comes in to buy forty shares . . ." she goes on, as the visitors listen to put the trading floor together like a vast jumbled jigsaw. "Who owns big business?" she asks rhetorically. "You own big business!" she cries out. "You own the stocks! You and you and you!" "Me?" a man asks and the girl doesn't listen.

One exit of the Stock Exchange opens onto New Street, a narrow, slightly curving street, threadneedling into lunch counters. Lunch counters feed the towering office buildings. But the men in Brooks Brothers tropicals, Madison Avenue fitted, who don't have to worry that lunch may go over 80¢, empty from the trading floor to drink martinis. Martini is the appetizer. Gin in any form, tonic, soda, lime, or Scotch on rocks, is enough to untie the stomach muscles. A good, healthy martini is 55¢ on New Street, made to order, poured into an Old Fashioned glass so that the shaking hands won't spill the gin over the rim. Nobody gets drunk. The ticker tape at the entrance quoting stock prices is a reminder that the day hasn't ended. The gin simply brings the men back to a happy state of normalcy. "How do you live so long?" the man in the gray tropical asks the short, fat produce broker at the end of the bar. "Easy. I get screwed three times before breakfast!" "You—three times! You dog, once and you'd wag your tail like a drummer boy!" "And you're the only guy I know who's spent thirty-five years perfecting one position!" The big man standing alongside with a green and white badge on his lapel says, "Nobody ever starts a fight in here. It's a lot of joking. Neither of them can get it up. What did they charge you for the beer?" and he points to my bottle of Blatz. Thirty-five cents. "That's a lot of money for beer. I wait until I get back to Jersey to do my beer drinking. The TV set going on a prize fight, the windows open, a swing on the porch, the set turned so that you can see it through the open window. In New York you'd have to climb out on the god-damn fire escape. I drink about six, seven tins through a fight. For lunch, you can't beat martinis. Yesterday I had four martinis. I went back to the office and had to sleep it off until 4:30. But try and think of putting some hot potatoes and a piece of beef covered with gravy into your stomach without a martini."

The restaurant off the bar is a huge, open room, the tables all occupied, smoke hanging above the eaters, waiters rushing with trays of food, men buttering rolls, slicing into prime roast ribs of beef *au jus*. "Gin! Do you know there's a 250 per cent dead profit on all bar whisky." "What do you think the total sale of whisky, I mean over the bar, would come to in New York in a single day?" "Oh shit, maybe millions, five, ten million," the man with a white button on his lapel thoughtfully estimates. "It's good tax money." A good-looking, graying man, his suit hanging with the needled care of every other suit, becomes philosophical. He turns to his friends beginning their second martini. "You know, my father was never able to teach me. And I haven't been able to teach my own son. I envy people who are gregarious. I guess it's born in a person. Though I guess it takes a lot of pressure off you if you're financially secure. Men with lots of money always seem to have that gregariousness." Two, three martinis seem to be the limit. The afternoon is long and who knows what a telephone call from San Francisco might bring.

The doorway off New Street leads down below the sidewalk into a buffet restaurant where men eat standing up, gathering in groups of twos and threes around tiny tiered tables. No martinis or Scotch, not even beer. A steady stream of men in the tan office jackets of Wall Street hurry down the stairs. There isn't a chair in the restaurant. One man forms a stiff arch with his body as he bends to bring the green pea soup up to his mouth. Two men form a luncheon date. One man chews on a cold fried egg sandwich. He wears a neat rayon tropical suit. His friend bends over the lamb stew, the gravy spilling. The chunks of noodles and ham, kidney stew, french roast, pork cutlet, have to be brought up to the mouth. Maybe it's healthier to eat standing up. "How's the house?" And you wonder, do these men own property? "I finally got it for eleven-five." "With the recreation room?" "No, I'll take care of that next summer." Why do the men crowd the buffet? To save money? Yes, but the thin sliced ham sandwich is only worth 15¢. Wall Street rises above the buffet. Big business is credit, a verbal contract is lasting, a man's reputation is his life—the receptionist told you all that at the Stock Exchange. And at the buffet after you finish bringing the green pea soup up to your mouth, the check has to be paid. But there's no check! Only the verbal contract of the market place. You tell the man at the cash register, 55¢. He yells out, 55¢. Nobody asks what you ate. "Eat 'em and beat 'em," maybe. But here at lunch time the great drama of credit is enacted—who knows, the "55" for stew and coffee can mean 55 shares of A.T.&.T.

The Washington Market works through the night. The food that feeds New York has to come from somewhere out of the ground, be transported to warehouses in the city where other dealers will come in trucks, haul the food off to grocery stores, supermarkets, the 19,000 restaurants, the Automat. Huge trailer-trucks choke the streets. Traffic is impossible down Washington Street. At night the men light bonfires to keep warm. An organ grinder comes to entertain as the trailer-trucks are unloaded and the produce piled up inside the vast commission houses. Lunch is a bottle of sherry at the end of a night of unloading. Sleep is on the sidewalk, sprawled out, tired from work, tired from the sluggish wine. The mahogany, brass-bound, mirrored, massive New York bars front West Street. Across from it the highway rises on a trestle, the freighters dock with dried mush-

rooms, bananas, English jams. From Chambers Street to Fulton
Street, spreading out further uptown, the commission houses keep
New York fed. Lunch in the West Street bars is a shot of whisky,
bottles of beer, Piel on tap. Nobody seems to eat. The menu reads:
fried chicken, smothered ribs, pork chops, stewed chicken, beef
stew, veal stew, hog maws, corn bread. No price over a dollar. Two
men silently watch the bartender fill a shot glass to the cut glass
strip, then happily pour a drop over. "I finally got wise to myself.
I rent out the damn house when I'm not there. At $35.00 a week
I don't have to worry about paying the damn taxes. I sublet and the
dough pays the taxes." "How do you like it out in Long Island?"
"It's all right if you get in with the natives. I've been there sixteen
years now, so I'm in with them. They'll do anything for you, just
give them a bottle of beer. You know the kind of guys they've got
out there. Just show them a plugged roof, they squint at it once and
know just what to do. I had a guy fix up the attic into a recreation
room for a couple cases of Ruppert, the cost of the lumber!" Twelve.
Twelve-thirty. One. Lunch is over. The hour passes quickly, men
talking knowingly about the other dumb half of the world.

Brahms' *Concerto in D Major for Violin and Orchestra* fills the air
of the mall behind the 42nd Street Library. Wires stretched along the
branches of the green trees carry the music through two twelve-inch
speakers. Heifetz is playing. The park benches are filled with typists,
clerks, thoughtful old men employed as messengers, who listen at-
tentively, nodding, faces reflecting the aged glory sometimes caught
by portrait photographers. The stenographers sit sprawling on the
stone walk, a sandwich packed at home is unwrapped, the waxed
paper carefully saved for the trash can. A container of coffee, a
coke, a milk shake, washes down the thick-sliced homemade ham.
Books are read to the music, one Negro girl thoughtfully turning
the pages of *Best Loved Poems*. The recorded concert is two hours
long, time enough for two shifts of the lunch hour. Two, three girls in
a circle make up a luncheon party. The junior editor sits on the stone
walk and talks about her magazine, nibbling on a salami sandwich.
"Do you know what they get for this?" and she holds the salami

sandwich up to her boyfriend, "65¢, with a couple of french fried potatoes added, a thin slice of pickle!" "You can't beat eating out here under a tree. This would cost you $6.50 on Park Avenue, especially with Heifetz playing." The park seems a slice of Paris. Particularly because of the midtown office girls who are probably the best dressed working girls on the globe. Thin silhouettes, scooped out necks, colorful flared skirts, the new open shoes, the girls bite into their sandwiches, measuring each bite against what they can save for a new outfit at Peck & Peck. Restaurant prices are too high on the 42nd Street and Fifth Avenue blocks, unless you crowd into the Automat, Bickford's, eat chow mein three times a week. The cost of a tip can cover the price of a container of coffee to go. The girls aren't alone. The men unpack hero sandwiches, an apple, a peach, fresh fruit for the diet. The Brahms concerto ends, Stravinsky comes on, the *Petrouchka Suite*. No piddling music.

"Have a cocktail with your lunch!" the top of the menu urges. "Like hell," a girl points at the menu, "55!" A "Business Girl's Lunch" on 36th and Seventh Avenue: tuna fish salad, tea and cake; chopped liver plate with lettuce and tomato; one meat ball, two vegetables; one stuffed cabbage, two vegetables. Martinis should run free out of water fountains between 34th and 40th Street on Seventh Avenue for the girls who pour out of the loft buildings into the lunch counters, the cafeterias. One cafeteria in the garment section makes the trading floor of the Stock Exchange look like a slow-motion Keystone cop chase. The crowds pile up in the doorway. One girl hands out silver, another trays, a shouting pile driver keeps the line moving. A vast spread of food hits your eye. Everything! Dairy, meat, blintzes, latkes, beef, lamb, veal, five, six soups, dozens of desserts, creamy whipped pies scooped up, thrust across the counter, bowls of borscht being balanced, coffee spilling over, a battery of cash registers take the money. Bright lights glare down. The interior decorator made the huge room *modern*. Leatherette, chrome, the slick paint, bounce the light. Try and find a table! An army of bus girls empties the tables as quickly as the food is devoured. Rush for a spot. The spilled-over coffee can be poured back into the cup. Once you're settled, eat with the roar of zipper quotations in your ear, piece goods, buckles, buttonholes, shoulder pads, figures in the hundred thousand to dress America. One bus girl cries out, "If I don't go crazy today, I never will!" as the dishes pile up. But today is exactly like yesterday and tomorrow.

Men find time to talk once a breast of beef sandwich has been washed down with a tall glass of iced tea. "I know, you know, Steve, a million guys may know, but you've got to take a test to prove what you know, otherwise you die a lousy operator!" "But the boss can see when a guy knows his job." "He sees! He sees only what he wants to see! You've got to take the test to get the union rating. Don't you ever feel it, Steve, the whole world is like that, a test, just like high school, you've got to prove yourself over and over again." One man finds time to sell insurance, shoving aside his chopped liver plate. "If you die, Milt, if you turn sick, you're not eighteen years old, you have commitments to your family. Let's face it squarely, a man has to own up to those commitments, you can't bury your head in the sand." "But I could never see—" "I know my own life, that's the only way I can talk. Once I got sick—I was twenty-eight then—so sick I couldn't get out of bed for days. But fortunately I was single, I had my mother to look after me. But what if I was married, had a wife, a family? How long do your savings hold out? The worst tragedy that can happen to a guy in this country who makes a fair living is to get caught up in doctor bills. You go, Milt, just like the race track or the stock market crash." "It's not as bad as all that." "No? That illness of mine taught me. At twenty-eight I thought I was as free as a bird. But a guy at thirty wants to marry. He sees layers of his life going away. He wants a home, a sex life. You get older and older, you just can't pick up a girl on the street. And then when you marry you see how important it is, the wife, the house, you don't want to ruin it all. Think it over, Milt, you have to live at a certain level of life up to commitments which your income will permit."

The girls come down the elevators. It's wonderful to see the warm, bright smile of recognition the girls use to greet one another in the lobby, grateful to see a familiar face for lunch. "Where are we going to eat?" "Schrafft's, where else?" On the sidewalk of 35th Street, the New York girls who don't have to worry about career girl rent, who make the long two-hour daily train ride from the Bronx, Brooklyn, are easily picked out by their accent, the high-style black dresses they wear, not seen in other cities unless you attend a wedding, the "Met" on its cross-country tour. The girls put their money into clothes, high-priced luncheons. "Supper, ma makes!" The menus they walk into begin at $1.10, a martini is 60¢. Weekends are spent in the mountains. "It cost us $25.00 from Friday to Sunday. But that's just the beginning. It's worse than New York. You've got to tip everybody, bus boys, chambermaids. You can't live unless you *smear!*"

In the lobby, men in shirt sleeves hurry to lunch. A sign reads: *No coat rule in effect from 8:30 a.m. to 6 p.m.* The stylists in big black round hats, tight dresses, brokers, designers, bosses, top-money salesmen, enter the dim café with the padded hum of piped music, talk of Paris. The menu begins at a price high enough to keep out the cutters, bushelmen. A hostess leads you to a table, the New York menu unfolds, endless choices of broilings, roasts, fish. But salami and eggs is a fondly remembered dish and only $1.10. Paris is talked about as though it were a suburb of New York. "Edith went to Paris and picked up seven new numbers." "How is the wedding line this year?" "The Paris numbers don't mean a thing. They all want to get married in the old numbers. October, November, it's all over." "Of course, Eddie. Didn't you ever stop to figure it out? People get married in June so that the kid will be old enough to run around in the park by the following summer. You have the diaper headaches during the winter." The drinking is light at the bar. The inevitable martini, a shot of whisky gulped down, a dill pickle stuffed into the mouth to take the edge off. In the lobby, truckers, clerks, elevator operators, messengers, the men who shove the hand trucks through the milling Seventh Avenue sidewalks, crowd a lunch counter. Knishes, apple pie, cold borscht, salami, Virginia ham. "Make the pastrami hot." A plank of wood nailed into the wall serves as a table. Pastrami sandwiches are carried over, hot coffee, a piece of Danish.

The waiters speak French east of Fifth Avenue in the 50's. The *maitre d' hotel* inspects your chef salad, thumping together the vegetables to earn his two dollar tip. The men eat in an enormous, high-ceilinged, gilded, soft-muraled room, leather armchairs, round tables, the imposing sign "Men's Café" keeping the ladies away. Silver coffeepots decorate the tables, heavy linen napkins. The men recognize one another by their tailors. The whole world of *maitres d' hotel* judge you by the way your collar falls, the leathery look of British shoes. Inspection day in the barracks. Lunch takes two hours, the *maitre d' hotel* writing down your order, handing it on to a waiter who brings the cold broth surrounded by ice cubes. A boy with a breadwarmer passes out hot rolls. The men look closely shaved, freshly showered, talcum-sprinkled. Madison Avenue, Park Avenue, Fifth Avenue are just around the corner and belong to the men who toss away the parsley on their boiled potatoes. Nowhere else in New York do men look so much in control of the twentieth century. Take off the double-breasted business suits, the loomed ties, put on a white toga or silk britches, a powdered wig, and you'll have the Roman patrician, the French courtier, the eighteenth-century man of London. Four men order fish. The waiter, with the permission of the *maitre d' hotel*, sets down a broiled garnished fish, a side order of french fried potatoes. "How about another order of these?" The big, heavy-set, rolling man takes up the french fried potatoes, stuffing them into his mouth. The waiters, the *maitre d' hotel*, look on with the faces of men who know that their tips are counted as income tax.

At last you begin to hear talk about the "21", the El Morocco. The men at the long bar of the men's café have entrée. "You bastard you, you old son of a bitch, you closed up with me at the El," the man in the white linen jacket is greeted. The South American smiles, "Yes, yes, we finished the night." "Marco's an old whore-monger," the man in the blue linen suit explains to his friends. "Come and have a drink." Coins are matched, heads or tails? "Two martinis, put it on my check." "I won, you big shit!" Hah, hah, everybody at the corner of the bar laughs. A big man with an explorer's mustache picks up the bar telephone. What greater thrill is there left in New York than having yourself paged at a bar? "I've got to get to the '21' for lunch," the man alongside keeps repeating. He's on his fifth Scotch and soda, weaving slightly. It's not good society to show your drinking, particularly at 12:30 in the afternoon. The $50.00 call girls begin to become real. "The whole story is that she married this guy and they busted up four days later. Now she's hustling her ass out in Yonkers." "She's got some ass," and the man with sandy brown hair waves his hands in the air, outlining the girl's body. "She's a beautiful piece of ass, beautifully put together." The telephone number in Yonkers is written down. Another address is exchanged. "Don't date these broads, just screw them, it's a lot cheaper." "Make me another gin and tonic—" The bartender is the only remaining authoritative figure. The quarter, fifty cent, odd-lot, change fills the mixing cup. Three martinis seem to be the limit before the men sit down together around the big white linen tablecloth to order chicken salad. The diced chicken breast, tomatoes, lettuce, is brought up from the kitchen by the waiter and the *maitre d' hotel* takes over, arranging the tomato slices, mixing the salad dressing into the chicken breast. Where are the big words? The big ideas? Who juggles the world? One man in a custom-tailored linen suit stands over his Scotch on rocks retelling his last great adventure. "You know what New York is on a Saturday in the summer. I stayed in town last weekend and had a wonderful time. I called up an old girl friend from Long Island. We had lunch at the Plaza, then strolled across the street to the Park and over later to the Savoy-Plaza where we had some drinks with music. After that we took in a movie and I was home by eleven. It was a wonderful day for New York."

The ideal is Paris. The East Side marquees invite you to tortoni, spumoni, seven-layer cake, filet of sole, venison, waitresses in black and white aprons. But lunch is lunch. At two o'clock the office telephone rings. The working population of Madison, Fifth Avenue, who make over $10,000 a year, need the lunch hour to open their hearts beyond the written contract; the chafing dish is merely a

substitute for the sun that can't get past the drawn taffeta drapes.
The East 50's lead you down soft carpeting, tall, gracious hostesses
who bend an elbow toward an empty table, mirrored bars, people
who comfortably look exactly like one another. Is the food good?
Two ladies in black hats drink away their lunch. Straight bourbon.
"Madame would like her table now?" "No, Louis—you know,"
the lady with black gloves up to her elbow says to her luncheon
friend, "you have so much of this food in you all the time. Food just
bloats. But this, when you drink this damn whisky down you let
everything out. God, what a happy discovery." "Sure." "People are
certainly made funny. Four ounces of whisky and you feel like Aris-
totle." Three men walk out of the CBS Building and stand undecided
on the corner of 52nd Street. Around them in a circle of walking
blocks are the restaurants of the world, French, German, Indian, Ar-
menian, Scandinavian, Chinese, Jewish, porterhouse steak. "Where do
we eat?" "21?" "Nope." "How about Nino's?" "Not today." "Did
you ever try the 500 Club?" "No." Across Madison Avenue, dodging
traffic, to talk over lunch the salesman's commissions on TV spots.

On 51st Street, three men just beginning thirty, just tasting the
blood of editorial high life, line up at the bar with a slim, sleeveless,
tall, healthy-faced junior editor. Three martinis, one dry sherry.
They stand at the bar of Toots Shor's as though they're in the throne
room of Aly Kahn. "I must tell you a story." "I have to comment
on that!" "No, I mean about commuting," the girl speaks up, "I
might as well live in Nyack. I took that apartment past Columbia
University, now it means going cross-town, changing." "The evils of
New York life." "How's the new picture coming?" "We're starting
publicity on it Monday. I saw the rushes yesterday. It's something.
You know, those older stars have something, a grasp of the screen,
that real hocus-pocus." "Oh, they're all whores or Lesbians!"
"That's a pretty loose puritanical tag." Another round of martinis,
the girl is coaxed into a fresh dry sherry. The tall boy's eyes aren't
used to two martinis before lunch. He begins to look like a wheeling
freshman. "Did I ever ask you," he says loudly, his drink spilling,
"what has four wheels and flies?" The most respected guy at the bar

comes in wearing a crumpled sport jacket, a loud plaid shirt, a color-splattered tie, an old pair of suit pants and orders a glass of water because it's too early in the morning to begin drinking. The restaurant is New York. You pay the price and eat roast beef. No battery of clothing experts linger in the foyer to determine your entrances and exits. You walk naked into the dining room and hopefully pray someday you'll get a nod of recognition from the bartender.

The Campaign

PAUL STOOD ON THE BLEAK WINDY CORNER WHERE THE district officially began. Down the drab side-streets ran the squared-off residential blocks, ill-kept, dim, gray, heated by steam, fed by credit grocery stores. Directly north ran the bus line, noisy, slow, crawling past the smoke-shops, lolling men, the poolrooms, cluttered dry goods stores, big ugly supermarkets—crowded, smelly, cash registers ringing—the noisy colored Bar-B-Q joints—hot sauce on black, charcoal-broiled spareribs—more dirty, bleak little shops, until the neighborhood came to an end with the final stop of the bus line.

On all sides, spread around in a politically bound triangle were ten thousand voters. In a blind, dumb way he knew that all of these people had their own personalities that he could never hope to reach in a political campaign—but there must be some point of contact. So many people. So many businesses. So many homes. Everybody had a place to sleep. Everybody trying. The meat market with the kosher meat sign. The meat market with the pork sausages hanging in a line like a corps of inflated ballet dancers.

"Giterman, I'm going to give you the campaign straight," Patty began stiffly. "You're not as wise politically as we are but you've got a lot of stuff on the ball. Certainly enough to beat out Consolo if you're smart enough.

165

"The way I see it, it's like this. A Jew against an Italian. No—don't get me wrong. I'm not talking up racial issues. I'm not even thinking of any kind of trouble. But this neighborhood is just about half-Italian, half-Jewish. And that's the way the votes'll stack up."

"I think I see what you mean, Patty," Paul started to say, carefully choosing his words. "But I don't think the campaign has to be fought on purely racial grounds. I think I've got a good enough record in the ward to beat out Consolo. But if Consolo starts to make it a racial issue, don't worry, I'll carry the ball—"

"I'm glad to hear you say that, Giterman. It'll make the campaign a lot easier. I've worked with Jewish people all of my life. A Jew is no different to me than whatever you want to pick out of the hat. But hell—let's not get involved in talking. You know how we stand."

Patty stood up ceremoniously. Giterman stood up. They shook hands.

"Hello Mister President!"

"His Honor, the Mayor!"

"Hello Councilman! Any free passes to the fights?"

Happy, excited, shouting, Paul's whole family was on hand for the meeting he had arranged. His cousins filled the living room and flowed over into the dining room where they nibbled on *lekach* and hard candy. Paul's mother sat in a corner of the couch, tired from having prepared a big meal for all of her relatives. Why couldn't they bring cold cuts? Who knows what a mother feels when her son is being feted? For nobody fulfills a dream. And a child is always a dream of its mother.

"What do you say, Paul," his Uncle Morris asked above the excitement, "are you going to change the face of the neighborhood?"

"If I get your vote eight times," Paul joked.

"There ought to be a law for us voting at least ten times!" his uncle joked back. "A special privilege for relatives!" The uncle looked at his nephew, proud, smiling. He remembered Paul when he was a baby. His little nephew running for councilman! The way the world moves, boom, swift. He used to hold him on his lap and say, *nu*, shine my shoes, you'll make your first dime. Now he could boast at the store, that little stinker, he used to wet my pants, now he's a councilman! Sure, free passes for anything. I'm his favorite uncle!

"Seriously," Paul said, addressing the whole group, "I'm going to need all your help. A councilman race is a private neighborhood affair. It doesn't involve the city, the state, the country. Just us. And sometimes the margin is so small that a couple of votes can swing the election. A simple majority, one vote. That's why all of you are going to have to get up as many pledges as possible. We'll ring doorbells—wake up the neighborhood—show them who the better man is!"

"Wheee!" Uncle Morris shouted. "He already talks like a politician!"

"Consolo is making a strong play for the colored vote," Patty told Paul at a party strategy meeting. "It's up to you now to out-promise him. Prove to those colored people that you'll look out for them in the City Council. Their vote may swing the election."

Paul nodded. He was beginning to feel the campaign. Move in quick, make a speech, strike out, make another speech, ring doorbells—talk! talk! talk! talk! talk! Talk to people! That was the most important thing.

Face-to-face contact. This colored business wouldn't floor him. Didn't he grow up in the downtown colored section. Weren't his first friends colored? He never felt that need in himself to say "nigger" —to talk down the colored people—to become as vicious as some people he knew. . . .

"Well, Paul," his mother asked him at supper, "how are you making out?"

"All right, Ma."

"And you think you'll be elected?"

"I hope so, Ma."

"And if you're elected—what then?"

His mother didn't wait for an answer. She carried the dirty dishes into the kitchen. She had begun to hear talk. Neighbors came over to the house. The other man wasn't going to let the election go so easy. Paul might get hurt. This new business! Mrs. Fine said they might cut Paul up, kick him in the belly, Mrs. Goldberg said, break his arms. He shouldn't drive around alone at night. The gangsters! They might come to the house. The trouble they could cause.

Paul left the table and sat down by the telephone and dialed Patty. This new business was unreal. Patty had mentioned it offhand. The opposition might have him beat up. Should he ask for police protection? No—that would only show that he was frightened. He still remembered his judo from the army. The side of your palm is the most dangerous weapon in the world. Let those punks get smart with him! He could see himself in action, the side of his palm cutting down goons, men falling all around him, his face sweaty, arms swinging, then somebody coming at him with a knife, a swift kick to the groin, the man going down begging to be let alone. . . .

"Hello! Hello!"

"Oh—hello Patty. This is Giterman."

"Hello Paul. What's new?"

"I'm just getting ready to make a speech at Stevens Hall."

"You'd better make it good. Consolo has hit that neighborhood with sound trucks day and night promising those poor bastards everything but the kitchen sink."

"I've got a speech I think will make the grade. Tell me," Paul asked, his voice dropping down to a whisper, "is there anything to the rumor that Consolo hired a couple of goons to take care of me?"

"No—Consolo wouldn't do a dumb thing like that. He's too smart a politician. But he has a lot of political bums hanging around his place. There's a possibility that a couple of wise guys might think that if they beat up a Jew he'll just vanish out of the campaign. I'd advise you to have a couple of guys in the car with you when you travel around. Don't travel around alone. It might set those punks thinking."

"How about police protection?"

"If you were anybody else, I'd say OK. But you're a Jew, Giterman. You can't forget that and police protection will go against you. They'll say you're afraid."

"I don't see where it makes any difference—"

"It's not what you see or think, Giterman. It's what is. And that's the way people think. Don't be afraid to swing a wrench. I won't keep you any longer."

Paul hung up. He walked into the foyer to get his coat. Oh those jeeps in the army with a machine gun on the hood. That's the kind of car he should drive around in. Brrumph—one burst! He still couldn't get down to the reality of it. Three men sitting in a room plotting to beat him up. It only happened in the movies. Nuts! Pick up any edition of the paper. He didn't want the election to hinge on whether he was a Jew or Consolo an Italian. Damn it, that wasn't the issue!

It rained on election day. The voters were late getting to the polls. Paul went from door to door urging the people to vote. The whole family took the day off to ring doorbells. They borrowed umbrellas and escorted voters through the rain, making sure that everyone who could vote, voted.

"Paul, if you win," Uncle Morris announced to the jammed living room, "I'm going to drink champagne for the first time since your *bris*. Look! I've already invested $6.98 for a bottle!" He held up the bottle and everybody laughed.

Paul's mother was busy in the hot kitchen looking after the *lekach*. Two cakes were still in the oven, three big honey cakes were cooling off on the kitchen table. *Lekach*, whisky, herring, the table piled high—it seemed like Paul's Bar Mitzvah all over again.

The neighbors shoved their way into the living room to pat Paul on his back. A baby—Paul Giterman who used to run around with his nose dripping—a Jewish boy from the neighborhood—he might be elected councilman. The radio would tell the news. The street needed another lamppost, more garbage pickups. . . .

Everybody shushed. The radio announcer was coming to Paul's name. "From Ward 21, late returns, Paul Giterman, 4,478; Alberto Consolo, 3,896." Everybody yelled. Uncle Morris, made his own private joke. "How can anybody hear my cork pop in all this noise!" Paul stood up on a chair, flushed, happy, smiling, shaking everybody's hand, laughing, crying. His mother came into the living room with a trayful of *lekach*, tears running down her face. A newspaper photographer took a picture of Paul surrounded by his neighbors and relatives. "Look," they all cried, "he's in the paper already!"

"You'll have to excuse me!" Paul shouted above the excitement. "We're having a victory celebration down at party headquarters. Eat, drink, be happy—and I'll be back as soon as I can, thanks everybody for your help!" Paul made his way through a room full of handshakes.

What to say now at party headquarters? What could he say except that everybody in the neighborhood had pitched in to do a terrific job. Now the important thing was to hold office. He felt that same overwhelming paternalism toward his voters that a bridegroom feels toward his bride while the marriage service is being intoned. Every rock, street, lamp light, garbage can, water plug, it all lay under his personal protection. Paul pulled up and parked his car opposite party headquarters. He could hear the singing going on inside.

"Hey fellow!" Somebody motioned to Paul from the sidewalk. Paul opened the door. A tall, heavy figure pulled him out of the seat. Before Paul could say a word the attacker had him down on the sidewalk, kicked him twice. Paul tried to rise. The stranger lifted Paul to his feet, struck him a heavy blow on the mouth. Paul fell back, crumpling on the sidewalk. The stranger lifted his foot to kick Paul again but just then a voice cried out, "Hey!" The man fled down the dark street.

The laughter stopped in the living room. Everybody felt nervous, dry, nobody knew what to say. The outrage! To make a victory, a celebration, such a cheap thing. They sat in mumbled silence waiting for Paul to come back from the emergency ward. . . .

It was past midnight when Paul walked into the living room. His suit was torn, one side of his face was bandaged. The phone rang before any of the newspaper reporters or neighbors could ask questions. "It's for you, Paul," his cousin announced. "Consolo would *like* to talk to you."

The people edged closer to the telephone in the dining room.

"Yes Al . . . Sure Al . . . No Al . . . Of course Al . . . You wouldn't do that Al . . . Sure Al . . . I know Al . . . Of course Al . . . Sure Al . . . Thanks Al . . . Sure—good-bye Al."

Paul hung up. A photographer snapped a picture of Paul by the telephone. The reporters and neighbors moved in close around him. They stood waiting. Giving him a chance to make the first statement. Paul looked at their faces. What to believe? What did they believe? Damn it! Why did it have to happen? He was sick that he couldn't have stood face to face with whoever slugged him, fought it out. It was so goddamn dirty to be beat up, thrown to the ground like you were dirt, kicked like a sick dog. Oh he'd like to find the bastard. . . .

"It's nothing," Paul said, looking at all of the faces surrounding him, addressing no one in particular. "Some cheap drunk lost an election bet and took it out on me. There's nothing more to the incident."

Paul's Uncle Morris held up a full bottle of whisky. "Well! what're we standing around for," he cried out, "this isn't a funeral! Let's drink to the new councilman!" He brought the whisky bottle down with an elaborate gesture and started filling the glasses that were eagerly pressed in front of him. "And *lekach*—the herring— there's a whole table of corned beef left—let's make this a real party!"

Somebody pressed a plate of potato salad, slices of corned beef and pastrami, a dill pickle and a smear of mustard into Paul's hand. The announcer on the radio was busy summing up the election results. "They had a special bulletin about your getting beat up," somebody buzzed in Paul's ear. He looked down dumbly on the plate of food.

Ooomphoooo—Paul said soundlessly. How big do you have to be? How big do you have to be before they don't dare knock you down—how big?

The Generations of Man

THE BUILDING STOOD, CRUMBLING AT ITS SIDES, ROOTED by iron spikes and oak beams, the red paint chipped, peeling, covering red bricks laid before the Civil War. He saw the four windows stretching across the width of the building and thought of the west wind that would blow in from Jersey across the Hudson River and cool him on hot summer nights. And then there was the west light but the west light had too much yellow and it would diffuse the stark pure colors he liked to squeeze from the aluminum tubes. One window had a north light. But he didn't need light. Only lots of space, a giant room large enough to stretch his arms in and walk, place things, his easel, chairs, a table, a rack for his paintings. . . .

Anything to get away from the piercing cries of the pushcarts, the gutted vegetables, the gangs of men, boys grown into men, unchanging, ganging up on the street corners. Anything to get away from his two-room cold-water flat on Sullivan Street, three blocks south of Washington Square, two rooms the size of a closet—in the summer the heat hung heavy, thick and solid there, and in the winter the oil from the heaters gave off the sticky smell of soiled rags. He had heard of painters living in a hall bedroom with only a cot and an easel, a rack built above the bed, no room except to move a brush.

Lately he found himself thinking of the big flopping books of wallpaper the paperhangers used to bring over to his house back in

172

Cleveland just before the holidays, and how the entire family would bend over the books on the kitchen table and make a selection, always asking his opinion because he was an *artist*. And then the paperhangers would go to work, the big bucket of paste, the long table and cutting tools, the strips of paper on the floor, messy, wet. But soon the rooms would smell fresh, clean, the paper bright on the walls. The smell came to him now, the pungent knowing smell of paste. People didn't paper their walls in New York. The walls rotted, year after year, blotched by flat sickly paint.

The smell of the paste and the remembrance of the flopping wall-paper books kept coming back to him, and along with it the odor of an open oven door, the Friday smell of sponge cake—and suddenly he knew that he had to get out of Sullivan Street, find a new place to live, an apartment where he could work and not be a victim of four flat white walls too thin to close out the shrieking mothers beside themselves over what to do with their fretting children—"Go to sleep you little bastard, you little son of a bitch, go to sleep!"

He began looking for an apartment the first day of his vacation. He had drawn an imaginary circle around the Village and every morning he would follow a different straight line to the periphery of the circle, knocking on every door. He had done the whole circle street by street in two weeks and nothing happened, only a few vacant cold-water flats, uninhabitable, dirty, grim, and apartments at rents only a fool would pay. And once a woman had led him into a room, past men sleeping in the carved-out niches of a railroad flat, a room curtained off by a piece of faded drapery and pulling aside the drapery she pointed to a cot tight against the wall, a little wooden shelf where he might put his shaving things and said, "This is the apartment, you like this?"

Tired at night from work and painting, knocking on supers' doors and seeing Goya-like faces coming to answer and shaking their heads, often with that smug idiotic *I'm in you're out*, he'd think of that enormous loft with high ceilings and big windows, endless space that he'd be able to make into the kind of place he needed to live in. They existed, huge empty lofts on the tops of buildings, but so far he had not been able to find his. He climbed high flights to empty lofts on

Fourth Avenue and felt the wonderful free space—but too many painters wanted the same thing and the rent had soared.

At night he dreamed of lofts, and he talked lofts to all his friends, until one day one of them told him about an agent who had a loft on Washington Street facing the docks near the Battery.

And now he stood, looked up at peeling red paint, the dangling fire escape, knowing that five flights up was an empty loft and he could have the loft if it suited him.

"What do you think?" the agent asked.

"The building looks all right."

"Like to take a look inside?"

The agent and Dave crossed the busy street. The front door pushed open and they started up the five flights. The stairs were wooden, freshly painted.

"It looks pretty good," Dave told the agent.

"Yeh, it does. We fixed it up since the housing shortage. The people were glad to find a place."

"How's the top apartment?"

"You'll see. I want you to see it for yourself."

On the fourth landing the newness changed to crumbling brick walls and warped stairs, blackened paint. A bulb hung above the dirt and dust. Dave took his hand off the railing and wiped the dirt free with the handkerchief in his coat pocket. He had already picked up the odor, the dank, heavy, smothering smell of a long-vacant flat.

"This is it," the agent said. He pushed open the door and Dave followed.

Dave stopped in the door and the odor of Sullivan Street seemed to pour out at him from the flat, Sullivan and Thompson, and the streets stretching east toward the river, roach-ridden, sunless, toilets in the hallway, no bathtubs, imprisoning people until they died.

"It can be made into something," the agent said.

Dave didn't answer. He stepped into the flat. He saw at once that there was no heat, no running water, no toilet, no electricity except the line running in from the hallway. The place probably hadn't been lived in for twenty-five years. The walls were scaly with age.

The west light broke through the smudged windows.

"The light is good," the agent said.

Dave didn't hear him. He stood in the center of the room feeling the weight of the floor underneath his feet. He was very tired. He thought of the circle he had drawn, the straight lines fanning out from Washington Square, the doorbells he had rung, flights of stairs climbed—

The agent's voice came through to him. "The place is in pretty bad shape but a little fixing up will make everything all right. We'll put up a toilet, set up the gas heaters and water. But the rest of the place will be in your hands."

In his hands. And he saw the walls of the squared-off cubicles ripped down, the place made into one great big enormous sprawling room filled with the sounds of the boats going up the river and the light from the sun, fresh paint, hot water and soap, clean lumber, the rotted linoleum ripped away from the raw planks, space and freedom, a full twenty-five feet by thirty feet on an island where land was sold by the inch.

"I'll take the place," Dave said, "if the rent is right. And I'll want a lease."

Two days after Dave signed the lease and paid his first month's rent he went up to the loft with a crowbar and a sledge hammer. He tested the walls to see how solid they were and then went to work.

The first blow of the sledge hammer shook the loft. The dust of twenty-five years exploded. The plaster crumbled and an opening in the wall appeared. He had three walls to rip down, and he went methodically to work, swinging the sledge hammer with deliberately placed blows, then using the crowbar to rip out the boards. The first night he tore down the wall that divided the flat into two bedrooms, and now there was a sense of space. He let the plaster and broken wood lie where it had fallen. The next night he returned and went to work on the wall that divided the sitting room and dining room. Instead of pounding away with the heavy sledge hammer, he used the crowbar, ripping apart the boards, salvaging them for a new wall that would make a kitchen for himself. That left one wall, and when he moved that back fifteen feet he would have the space he wanted. The boards were tough, held together by the years. Unlike the plaster, they didn't crumble. He spent the night at it and only succeeded in taking down half of the wall. But already the space was shaping up. He could see the dimensions of the room, the vast floating free lines.

It took two weeks to knock down all the walls and remove the debris. For days the room remained piled high with broken plaster and rotted lumber, the layers of linoleum he had wrenched off the floor. But when the plaster and filth had been carted down the five flights, a bushelful at a time, and the lumber, tied in lengths, carried down with the aid of two friends, the room stood revealed, the west light of the sun filling the great square.

The plumbers arrived soon afterward and installed a toilet, a sink, and a stall shower. And then Dave took the lumber he had salvaged and hammered together a new wall to enclose the kitchen; and a day after that he left his cold-water flat and moved in his belongings. For the first few days he slept in a dust-thick corner too exhausted to do more. He had still to paint the walls and re-surface the ceiling, install electric lights, scrape the floor, fix the windows, re-surface the kitchen, mop up the dust. But he no longer had to listen to the Friday night drunks scream out their *Holy Marys* or feel the intolerable weight of the gaunt, barren, big-breasted bodies as they lumbered up the stairs on Sullivan Street.

Now at night he only heard the trucks and occasional voices that yelled loudly and then vanished. The boats were never silent. He was solitary, except for the night sounds from the world below on Washington Street, one block away, where the boats unloaded their cargoes, and on the street, building after building, crates were piled high with the produce that fed the city. He could see only a glimpse of the Hudson River. A squat commission building blocked the water, hid all but the funnels of the ocean liners that docked midtown. He would finish the room in clean, straight lines, to make it a part of the water outside, the restless flow. The room would never be fixed. He'd be free to move, claiming space as he required it. Didn't what he would do as a painter depend on what he did when he stepped forward, improving as he stepped forward on what he had never known how to do before?

But the work went slowly. Tougher than he had imagined. The lights and the ceiling were the hardest job. And after he re-surfaced the walls, blotting out the bleak, rotted wood with burlap stretched tight and painted white, he built a rack for his paintings and hung his best work on the fresh walls.

One day he received a letter from his father in Cleveland that made him stop work. He read and reread the letter trying to under-stand what lay beyond the words. His father wrote only that he would be in New York at the end of the month. No particular reason, ex-cept that he'd like to see his son again. Dave sat on a chair and watched the letter in his hand shake as a subway train rumbled under the building. The smell and sight of the bucket of paste, the flopping wallpaper books, came back to him, the street lined with a double row of trees, scrubbed porches, where nothing ever seemed to happen yet people lived whole lives through.

He had been hammering away at the apartment for eight months and it still didn't look done. Now he had only two weeks to finish the job. Dave crumpled the letter and began to work. He began by scraping the floor of his living room, washing the windows, and then started to tack the rest of the burlap on his bedroom walls. The kitchen he left to the last, for everything would have to be painted white.

He had little sleep during the two weeks. Barely enough to keep him at his job and only with difficulty, for his work was painstaking, exact—commercial art. It paid him enough to live. The night before his father was to arrive Dave flopped into bed and slept clear through to the next day. The long sleep freshened his body and by the time he had shaved and dressed he felt ready to greet his father.

The train came in on time and Dave kissed his father, taking him by the arm, grabbing his suitcase with his other hand.

"How's everybody?" Dave asked.

"Good. They'll live," his father said. "But what about you? You don't write. . . ."

"How was the ride?"

"Better than the train I took from New York to Cleveland forty-five years ago. I would like a cup of coffee. . . ."

"There's a good cafeteria across the way."

Dave and his father had a cup of coffee and buttered tea biscuits and then stood on the corner of Fifth Avenue and 42nd Street.

"The world has changed," his father said.

"For better or worse?" Dave asked.

"It's changed like all things, for some better, for some worse. Now that I've seen the big buildings let's go up to your place. I'd like to wash, lie down—"

Dave stopped a taxi and they rode down Fifth Avenue, cutting over west to get to Washington Street.

"You know, Pa," Dave began, "New York and Cleveland are like two different worlds. You just don't have the same conditions. What you find in New York you won't find anywhere else."

"I know they're two different places," his father said.

"It's more than being just two different places. It's two different worlds. Especially the way the people live. Big rents, low rents. Fantastic apartment buildings, slums next door—"

"It's the price of the land that does it," his father said. "Not the *meshugass* of the people. It was like that when I came. The city made me sick. We got off the boat near the neighborhood where the Statue of Liberty is. So much filth. Rotten buildings, people hanging from the windows. I saw them when I stood on the sidewalk watching my bag, afraid that somebody would run off with it. I took a look at New York and didn't like what I saw."

The taxi turned into Hudson Street and continued south until Chambers Street.

"Why are the streets so empty?" Dave's father asked.

"It's Sunday, Pa, there's never any traffic in this neighborhood on Sunday."

"This neighborhood—" The taxi turned toward the waterfront. Foghorns cut the air. The elevated highway stuck out and beyond, the bleak gray docks, bolted, deserted.

Dave's father didn't say anything. He looked out on the neighborhood, the harsh brute warehouses.

"The next street, driver—right near the corner."

The taxi came to a stop and Dave paid before his father could reach for change.

"This is where you live—"

"It looks out on the water, Pa. Let's go up."

The newness of the paint on the ground floor made it easy for Dave's father to walk up the first flight of stairs.

"Who lives here?" he asked, motioning to Dave to stop and take a rest on the second landing.

"Mostly painters. The people on the first two floors are painters and the fellow right below me is a painter. And there's a seaman in the house, he paints a lot, too, but most of the time he's away. He likes to keep his place though. . . ."

"Painters," his father said. "Artists—" He started up the third flight feeling the strain of the climb on his heart. He had a heart good enough for plain ordinary walking, going from the house to his business, a chicken store just three short blocks away from the house, but this climbing, going straight up in the air like a balloon, it was insane. The heart wasn't made to climb steps like a monkey. He looked at his boy two steps above him. Could he climb the steps fifteen years from now? Would he want to? He wasn't a chicken any more. Years catching up. God, it doesn't stop. Up, up, up. Who built a house like this? Maybe this was the house he had seen from the street, the red brick and the red faces, people in long underwear.

"One more flight, Pa."

"I won't go down for a week. Let's stop again."

"You won't have to go down, Pa. You can see the whole city from the roof. This is the neighborhood that makes New York breathe. Banks—wholesale food—"

"But no shelter—" His father tried to catch the words but they came out. No sense in saying anything until he saw how his son lived, inside—how did he live inside? To be an artist. To fly. So— this was close to the clouds.

Dave had heard the words. Dammit, no he wouldn't talk any more, his words hung in his mouth, every phrase apologetic. It was his house, his house, his house! But it was also his father, his father, nobody else's father, this man alongside of him, not so tall now, a little bent, hair blackened-white, trying hard for breath, holding on to the railing—because of this man, imagine it, he had been brought, flesh and blood, into the world.

"Just one more flight, Dave?"

"One more, Pa."

"Let's go. And then I'll want a cup of tea."

Dave opened the door and his father stood in the doorway as he himself had done ten months ago.

"It's big," his father said. "A big room. A big room. . . ."

"C'mon in, Pa, you'll see how really big."

The west light hadn't failed Dave. It shone through the four windows flooding the room, lighting the paintings. His easel stood in the far corner, the west light falling on a painting he had done years ago, a romantic painting he considered it now. His father had always liked the painting. "It has a heart," his father had said to him, "it has a heart."

"Sit down, Pa," Dave said. "And I'll get some tea on the fire."

"You don't have to ask me twice."

Dave filled the kettle with water and rinsed out two cups and saucers, placing them on the table in the studio room.

His father sat down on a chair, stretching out his feet. He unbuttoned his jacket and loosened his shirt. And then he let his mind take in the room. He looked around the room at the high white burlap walls, the paintings, colors set down with force, tense against one another, the easel and on it the painting of people stumbling through rain, the windows bright with the Jersey sun, more paintings and then the rack built from floor to ceiling holding all of his son's work, years and years of it from when he first began to *potchke*.

"Was it like this when you moved in?" his father asked.

"No, it was a rotten hole when I moved in. Nobody had lived here for the past twenty-five years."

"It looks good—very good."

"It's what the city has come to, Pa. People just don't have a place to live."

"Then why do you stay here?"

"Because I think this is the place where I have to be."

"It's a good enough reason. Is the tea done?"

Dave got up and came back with the teakettle, steam pouring out of the spout. He poured the boiling water over the tea bags and brought one of the cups over to his father.

His father blew on the hot tea and then sipped from the cup.

"You don't write, Dave. We don't know from one month to the next what's happening to you. Have you forgotten all about us?"

"No, I just didn't write."

"How is it being a painter in New York?"

"No different from Cleveland. You just paint and paint."

"But do people come to see your work—all of the way down here?" And his father spread his hands and waved them toward the waterfront, the office buildings stretching south, the market and crates of vegetables.

"That's why I made the place the way it is," Dave said. "I wanted a place big enough where people can see my work. Where I can get a good look at it myself."

"And in the end—" his father asked.

"In the end—"

"And in the end, what are the paintings?"

"You live, Pa," Dave said, standing, getting rid of his teacup on the table and moving over to the window. "You live out a life—what else can you do?"

"Yes, you live out a life. You live," his father said. "You're right, Dave. What else can people do?"

Dave switched on a light by the window that illuminated the painting on the easel. His father looked again and remembered the painting as Dave had brought it down from the attic, the colors still wet. He knew then that his son wouldn't make money as other people made money.

"More tea, Pa?"

His father nodded his head, still looking at the painting. Dave picked up the empty cup and filled it in the kitchen. When Dave came back into the studio his father was standing, looking much taller than he imagined him to be.

"You haven't asked me why I came to New York," his father said.

"I thought you would tell me."

"I'm only twice your age now," his father said. "In the beginning I was everything. Now you're catching up. With your own two hands. You don't remember the chicken store when you were a baby and you'd lie in a basket on the floor while your mother and me would try to make a go. You learn a lot in a city like New York. I can't talk any more like a father. It would sound foolish. But we were worried about you. The whole family. Painting, painting, painting, painting, I'm not your enemy, maybe some day something will happen with your paintings. We know the history of the world. But we wanted to see you married, a wife, children."

Dave didn't interrupt. He waited for his father to continue. He listened.

"I know about New York. I once tried to live here. It almost crushed me like a chicken breast. It's hard to meet girls in New York. I know that, too. Ma met a girl, a very fine girl, a girl with a head, she reads books, talks intelligently. She'd like to meet you. Her name is Esther."

"Esther—"

"She looked at your two paintings, the paintings you left on the wall in the front room and asked about you. Ruth had a bridge party at the house—so Ma told her your whole history—"

"No girl would live in a place like this."

"No girl—your mother worked in a chicken store. No girl—a place like this. Why not, Dave? You made a kitchen. You made it beautiful. Look at the stove you bought. For what? You know, Dave, maybe I'm an old man but I think you'd like to get married. Make this your home, not a garret. An artist shouldn't stay away too long from his home."

Dave heard the words and wondered how they had come to his father. Why not? Was there so much distance between them? The west light from the Hudson River had turned into a purple haze with streaks of yellow still hanging in the sky. The room was almost dark. The smell had left, that dank uninhabited smell. He looked around at the walls he had finished, the white paint soft on the burlap, the rough-hewn floor, wide planks brought up from an American forest, cut and sized before his father's boat had docked in the Hudson River. And then he looked at his father. "We know the history of the world." He'd like the oven door open now, chicken soup simmering, that complete smell of fresh-baked sponge cake, a wife. . . .

He'd go down, Dave thought, and get a pumpernickel bread and some creamed herring in the delicatessen, and he and his father could sit down together on the couch and mix the pumpernickel into the creamed herring and eat and talk.

The Voices

JENNIE ASKS YOU TO SIT DOWN ON THE CLUMSY MA-
hogany chair covered with an afghan picked up at a Second Avenue
thrift shop. Outside, Lexington Avenue displays its individuality in
custom windows of yellowed Lautrec prints, LP records, puffed
cream pastry, basting stitches sewn on dummy models, prime red
beef to be delivered through the service entrance. "Coffee?" Jennie
asks. Yes. The room shakes as the IRT express train rushes past
underground. For an instant you wonder if the purplish walls will
hold, the building crumble. Not seriously but curiously. Curious,
as you see Jennie trying to hold back the shock waves as though
they're her personal embarrassment. You know how peaceful she
would like the entire world to be. Often you think of her as a Hasidic
zaddik; the inside of her soul is so naked, yet so complicated—
grasping further than where shots of sodium pentothol, insulin
coma, electric shock, free association, have left her.

"Zus," Jennie tells you, "I remember at home in St. Louis there
was a sweet little man with a puzzled face who would often laugh
and giggle when no one else was laughing or giggling and if one of the
boys on the street would yell at him or throw a rock, he would run
across to his porch or into the side door of his house, frightened, his
body hunched over. His face would become gentle when he could
talk to us or tell a little story, the wildest stories, often incoherent,

184

but the sound of the words were all that mattered, and they certainly came straight from somewhere inside of him. He had his ways of making up to us. In the summer, sitting on the porch when the lemonade was being served, waiting patiently for his glass, holding it up into the air in a toast to the cold ice and cooling lemon juice. We used to gulp our lemonade down. I don't know what's become of him. He's probably institutionalized now. When you move away from a neighborhood the events seldom catch up with you."

There are no porches in New York, only terraces, balconies, rooftops, fire escapes, garden flats, open windows that bring in the noise and dirt of Lexington Avenue. Lemonade is rarely served. Beer is brought up in quart bottles from the delicatessen. Red wine, a marked-down bottle of sauterne, chablis, martinis, coffee if the evening is late. "Do you know what, Zus?" Jennie goes on while the coffee is boiling. "At home everyone thinks I'm an intelligent girl who *just* had a nervous breakdown. How could I tell anyone in St. Louis about four years of analysis? They wouldn't understand. Just as we couldn't understand what that poor devil of a psychotic was trying to tell us kids. I suspect that all he wanted was to make himself known to us—and a little kindness and understanding. That's it, Zus. If it was only possible for psychotics like him and myself to make ourselves clear to the analysts. But there's no language now, no words, nothing in the psychoanalytic vocabulary to make communication, just the entire body of a *looney* like myself trying to live. Look at this crazy place!"

Three rooms, a bed, a grand piano stuck in the living room, oils, pastels, a piece of sculpture, a modern lamp, tables picked up at auction on University Place, an enormous oak secretary rubbed down to its natural wood, covering one whole wall just because it looks beautiful. The typewriter has six lines of a poem on *ruach*. Dust on the piano. Roaches crawling over the exposed pipes, the woodwork peeling from too many coats of paint, turned yellow by the three-burner iron Peerless stove.

"Sometimes I wonder what I live for. It's so funny, you know. Two adult people jabbering to one another, talking to your analyst once a week. Talk, talk, talk! You don't seem to have any meaning left, just a talking machine repeating old facts. The pity is that even the analysts forget how to listen to the sound of a human voice. You say *door*, they immediately think *vagina*. But you hope that maybe they'll learn enough from you to save other poor devils. If it wasn't for that, Zus, I would have quietly cut my throat long ago. I guess we all live to keep the world going. The worst thing is that you feel so cut off from your family, the people around you, really cut off in a big way. Isn't it a pity that life is such a one-way ticket?"

It's quite possible that nowhere else in the world are people so willing to talk about their analysis. Maybe it's the cement sidewalks. The subway tunnels. The self-operating elevators, the doormen, the tiled hotel lobbies, the Louis XIV chairs. Or that New York is bottomless.

Howe invites you to Fifth Avenue high on the eighteenth floor. His terrace overlooks Central Park; the skyline of 59th Street is a clay pigeon. Handsome books, a Renoir, a Utrillo, line the pale green walls. A deep-beige rug covers the seven rooms. A butler in a white summer jacket brings in broiled chopped sirloin, diced carrots, broccoli, cut glass filled with ice cubes. A button under the rug summons the butler for dessert. Cantaloupe. The hi-fidelity LP machine plays a Mozart quintet. The dining room window looks out on Central Park. All the windows open as doors onto the terrace. "You aren't fooled," Howe smiles, "I'm gay, homosexual. It's not the most terrible thing in the world, you know." What can you say? Of course you know he's homosexual, knees accidentally brushing, hands lingering too long for an ordinary handshake. On the terrace Howe looks down the eighteen floors into the brick alleyway. "Sometimes I think I should go right over the edge. That would be it, wouldn't it?" The indulgence takes only a reflective minute and then you ask, what does your analyst say about all this—and he knows you mean the Renoir, the fruitwood bookshelves, the mind that can't come to terms. "Say? I've only been with my analyst for three years. It's not that easy. You don't change a life in three years, Zus. But I think I know what will happen. Like the *Arabian Nights*, have boys, have girls. Isn't that what all the experts are agreed on? The body wants to relieve tension. Down there is the biggest relief," and he points again to the brick-walled service entrance eighteen floors down. "But out there is New York," and he points to Central Park, the reservoir the real estate brokers boast about in the Sunday ads. "C'mon, I'm going down to my analyst this afternoon. Ride down with me."

The analyst is in the East 60's. You wait at the open air cafeteria in Central Park. How long is a session? One hour. The seals dunk themselves in the water. The feathered birds screech. The lions and tigers are asleep. At six-thirty Howe comes up the walk from 59th Street. His face has a serious smile. Three times a week, $20.00 a visit, but money has never been a problem when the body needs relief. "I told my doctor how I wanted to make you all afternoon at the apartment, even in the taxi ride down. I lay there on the couch and boasted about it to my analyst, how I wanted to kiss you and make love just because you were a man and alone in the apartment. That was the big test for me, Zus. Talk is cheap, Zus, particularly if you know anything about psychoanalysis—and who isn't a self-appointed expert? The real test is when you know you come up against your problem and you can beat the thing out of your consciousness."

Where can you scream out? Perhaps as a subway train comes braking into the Times Square station. Some unhappy people shout on the subway platforms, others walk through the trains talking to themselves. In Washington Square men always speak to the trees, for only the trees will listen. On Charles Street the rooming house has a series of bells. The girl rings your bell. In some Village rooming houses you know your neighbors in a week. In others the doors remain closed, seldom do you see a face, only noises, telephones ringing, typing, the coughing of an old man waiting for his relief check. The girl doesn't live in the rooming house. "I'm sorry," she smiles, "I rang the wrong bell." The girl has black hair, dark eyes, a small, thin body, the wide, open intelligent look of the girls you see in the Village. A minute later up in your room you hear wild screams, terrible screams, a girl's voice, ranting, moaning, exorcising the devil, crying out in long stricken moans. At first you think of calling the police. But no one in the rooming house stirs. The screams

begin to sound like the girl's voice in the hallway. And then they
end. What the hell, you have to stand in the hallway to see what
went on. The girl comes out, a flushed, drawn look on her face. The
next day more screams. A man's voice. The Village! Flagellation,
perhaps a society has gathered on Charles Street. A few days later the
girl returns. Her screams last about fifteen minutes. How can you
ask a person, was that you screaming on the second floor? But then
Irv hears the same screams and he smiles, "It's therapy. No beatings.
There's a psychologist in the room and he lets the girl scream as
long as she likes. The guy should really work in a soundproof room.
It's a special therapy for people all tensed up. The screaming is
supposed to get some of the tightness out of them."

As you move over the city, looking for three rooms instead of two,
a tiled bathroom, hot water always on tap, the new neighbor across
the hall knocks on the half-open door. "Hello, I'm your neighbor.
If you need anything, just ask me." I will. "Maybe you can help me
out. My friend says there's no such thing as American philosophy.
Would you know anything about it?" He looks into the room and
sees the boxes of books piled up, the paintings ready to be hung, the
copy of Blau's *American Philosophic Addresses* on the kitchen table.
Sure there's an American philosophy. There's philosophy when two
people get together. The neighbor laughs. "Are you a painter?"
No. "I'm a painter. You'll have to come across the hall and see some
of my work. But right now I haven't been doing too well. My
analyst says I haven't been too fair with him." And then the story
of the analysis comes out when you cross the hallway. Leaning up
against the top of the maple dresser you hear the entire history of the
analysis retold as a penitent crushes his body with glacier rocks. The
mother looming as the evil figure. The early beatings by the boys in
the neighborhood. The first love affair with an older man in the cellar
of a house in Hartford. Love could only be had with boys. You
wonder what it is that turns the mind like a philodendron's leaf
toward the sun.

Flocks of young men come up to his apartment at night, boys in
black turtle-neck sweaters, denim work pants, dancers, actors,
writers, file clerks, painters, art student models, waiters, rich boys,

most of them hesitant about the way they have to face the world. Pots of coffee are made on the iron burner. The talk goes on until three, four in the morning. Always—after the art, the books, Mozart—mother is spread-eagled on the kitchen table, an orgy of word-whipping goes on. A dancer from Des Moines lives with the neighbor and together they paint the kitchen green, hunt the antique shops for copper pots. One night the smell of gas awakens the second floor. The neighbor comes over in the middle of the night, trembling. "Why did he want to kill himself? I gave him a bed. I didn't ask him for rent. Why would he want to die? I get so frightened, so sick of my life. I ought to give up painting, give up the Village, get away from New York, go back to Hartford, try to live like some of the people on my mother's street." Getting away doesn't always do the trick, you can only say. "I know—and I don't expect anything more from analysis. With people like me analysis goes on forever. There's no cure for life, only for neuroses. I'm in it, in it up to my neck. But I don't hate my father! I don't hate my mother! I don't even hate the neighborhood I was born in. How do you get caught up? Maybe it's painting. Painting tears you down. You wonder and wonder if what you're doing makes sense. You gamble a whole life. For what? A painting that's supposed to stop life, be outside of life. *How?* I need one of those jobs where you work hard all day long. The symphonic programs on WNYC can take care of all my crazy energy."

And you wonder, where does it break down, the concern to be a shadeless shadow of every other person; as unique as Plato writing down the *Symposium*. Seventeenth Street west of Eighth Avenue is not one of the most beautiful streets in the world. From the sidewalk you can just make out a light in the room. Garbage cans line the entrance to the building. The furnace is at the end of the long hallway. "It's an apartment," Eleanor cries out, "it's away from my lousy family!" Red wine is poured out of a gallon bottle. Helen stretches out on the studio bed. If you open the living room door the fumes from the furnace choke you. "I love living down here in the cellar," Eleanor calls out. She's high on wine. Her thin wiry legs show blue veins. How old is she—twenty, twenty-one? Helen on the bed is eighteen. "Lizzie, Lizzie, Lizzie, Little Lizzard, that's me!" Eleanor cries and runs over to the studio bed to kiss Helen, taking her up in her arms as a man would. "You beautiful son of a bitch," and she kisses her again. On another studio couch, Morrie lies alone, his face turned toward the wall. The red wine is at the half-gallon mark. Once he began to cry when he talked about his analysis, his slipping back into housekeeping with a lover who exploited all he earned as a math teacher. "Lizzie, Lizzie," he calls out, "you don't know what you're talking about. One glass of red wine opens your mouth like a sewer." "You shut up!" "And you can listen!" "Listen to what? There're the damn books on the shelves. Freud, Krafft-Ebing, Stekel! Do you think I'm like you, moaning and pissing over my analysis. I know what's wrong with me. I like girls. I love Helen. Let any man try and take her away from me. You can blame my beautiful stick-of-ice of a mother, my sick, weak, pissass dominating father, but don't yell at me!" Morrie turns his face to the wall. Order of fried eggs and bacon on 38th Street. Eleanor takes the order, sets up a knife and fork at the 38th Street lunch counter. Money doesn't grow on trees, bills have to be paid for the basement flat. In the evening she and Helen walk hand in hand through Washington Square Park. "They tried to mix me up once," Eleanor continues to cry out, standing over Morrie. "I talked and talked for five sessions and learned what I am. The world isn't going to change for me. So I make my own world. And I made Helen all by myself. And nobody will ever take her away from me, no psychoanalyst, no butch, not her family, nobody!" What does Helen do all day with her life? She types payrolls for an export firm on Wall Street.

The voices break above the noise of traffic on Madison Avenue, slips of speech during an intermission at a Town Hall recital, even while waiting for a Monday night lecture to begin, voices among people you'd least expect to talk about their psyche as freely as an appendectomy. The girl examines your admission ticket to a lecture class at the New School. The next time, you stop and talk. She plays with clay, making glazed ash trays. Abstract painting has given dignity to people's puttering with colors. Why don't you sit in with the class, you ask, instead of taking a seat against the wall? "Oh,

I feel kind of left out as a ticket-taker. And that's exactly what my analyst warned me against. You have to mingle with people in order to relate to them. You just can't wish it in your mind." What about the professor, do you ever feel like disagreeing with her? "Oh her! She thinks the entire world is an Oedipus situation!"

In the park, a friend sits puffing on a pipe. "My analysis is done," he announces as though he's just finished paying off his Buick. Done. Finished. "Finished. It took me two years and seventeen weeks." You want to ask, what do you do now? But the question doesn't have to be asked. The world is just outside the park. At a party on West 88th Street, the secretary talks up. "See, I'm supposed to be more aggressive. And I am aggressive when I disagree about Jean Gabin's acting in *Pepe Le Moko*." The secretary's face is all smiles at the sudden discovery of herself. Plots of Charlie Chaplin, the Marx Brothers, half a dozen remembered French films, analysts, fill the night, empty bottles of beer. "I had to quit writing scripts for a while," the hostess speaks up, "to get myself cleared. I went from one analyst to another up and down Central Park West riding the leather couch circuit. You know, when you're a writer you think you're pretty clever, even if it's only radio shows. It's like a long-winded soap opera the way they dig down into your past— uncensored of course by NBC officials." "And I'm just beginning," the secretary announces. "It's funny to think you're just at the beginning. It's a little like being born with everything but yourself."

Rents are too high in New York for most girls to manage more than $50.00 alone. And the silence of the rooms too quiet for sleep at night. Hilda found Margaret by placing an ad in the *Times* under the "apartments to share" listing. Hilda was paying $72.84. Margaret cut her rent in half. Where did Margaret come from? A furnished room on West 74th Street. At first you feel a stranger when you share a flat. You're not quite sure about turning on the lamp. How much of the two-room flat is really yours? Whose friends are whose? You sit stiffly on the studio couch listening to the talk of the corner of the world the people in the room live in, only opening your mouth to excuse yourself when you go into the small bedroom that you know is your own. "My analyst," Margaret begins one night, surprising everyone. What does such a quiet, southern voice have in its experience to call up during a psychoanalytic session? "My analyst said that the Ego determines psychosis, no I mean the Id, if the Id overwhelms the Ego, then you have a psychotic situation." "Do you think they know what the hell they're talking about!" Paul shouts. "Of course they know," Margaret says, her voice almost rising in anger, "if the psychoanalysts don't know, then who does know?" "Nobody knows, nobody, the whole psychic world is a mystery." "I'm afraid," Margaret dares to say, "you're the mystery, not psychoanalysis." "That's what you have now, people believing in a new God, a crutch, fakers getting $20.00 an hour for digging into your insides." "Did you ever go to an analyst?" she asks Paul. "No, thank God. I need my money for rent." "Then you don't know. You shouldn't speak if you don't know. You know they've helped thousands and thousands of people who are sick through no reason of their own. Go down to a psychiatric clinic in New York. See how they treat cases of little children. One little boy frightened by the color white during an operation, shocked out of his senses so that he can't even speak. See how they spend two, three years treating such a child, bringing him back into the world, reclaiming him for his family." "What about the girls you meet in New York? Every second girl giving her salary to a Fifth Avenue psychoanalyst. You live on beans and salads at the Automat and get nothing back but a lot of jargon, your own mother to use for a punching bag!" "You don't know how ignorant you are! New York has over a hundred-fifty psychiatric clinics, free clinics, hundreds of guidance clinics for retarded children!"

Lillian opens her package. "It's for *him*, Mahler's *Des Knaben Wunderhorn*. I don't know, I feel that I have to bring him a present. He's such a wonderful guy. See," she laughs, "a Freudian twist. He's such a wonderful guy—*Youth's Magic Horn*." The recording sells for $7.00 at rock-bottom cut-rate prices. Who gives presents to a doctor? But with Lillian you don't ask such questions because you like the way she happily places herself squarely in the middle of New York. "I was as mixed up as hell until I met my analyst. It's crazy in a way. You think it's just in your mind and after a while you're pretty damn sure that it is in your mind." And she isn't ashamed to say what was in her mind before analysis. "It's a funny business of not being close to your mother. Not really being close to anyone for that matter. You lay a few guys and they talk about being in love. You drive in cars and hang your feet over the open window letting the ocean wind from Jones Beach cool them off. Make trips upstate. Check into cabins, motels, go at sex again. Sometimes you feel like you're married, taking showers together, running the car over to the market, buying breakfast. But nothing turns you. Why? you ask yourself. And after a while you don't want to lay anyone. The guys you date bore you. You just want to close your eyes and sleep, no matter where you're at. Lots of people talking about book reviews, Broadway plays, Village gossip, but you just close your eyes and sleep. At first it looks cute. Just to be able to doze off at a party. But then you wonder. What the hell, you've read enough Tolstoy to know what life is like." Her apartment on East 81st Street has four rooms. Big brownstone walk-ups, housing thousands of subway riders. Out of one window you can get a glimpse of the East River. Lillian is subletting. "Look at this place, Zus! Four rooms—I feel like a whore up here. The guys come and I'm all alone. So what if I give my analyst $20.00 a week. It all comes back in income tax deductions. I don't plan any sudden trips to Europe. Clothes I have enough of. But the other thing, what you think the hundreds of people around you *do* have, a mind that belongs to you and not some crazy quirk that began when you didn't have the resistance to know what it was all about, that I don't have. Do you know what makes neurotics happy? They're happy they're not psychotic. Christ, it's a mess."

Not everyone you meet in the Village, the upper West Side, the East Side, is going to an analyst. The Hudson River isn't far from Flora's room. The landlord calls it a one-and-a-half. The bathroom, sink, dinette, cupboard space, closet, hallway, take up a space 9 x 10. A Paul Klee print hangs on one wall, a da Vinci drawing clipped from *Life*. A mobile floats from the ceiling. The living room is filled by a three-quarter bed. The fireplace doesn't work. When the landlord renovated the tenement he had the fireplaces designed to resemble Swiss chalets. It only meant an extra sack of cement, a 2 x 4 beam across the ceiling, to create a Village studio. The rent is $52.75 and it's a thousand miles away from Illinois. "How do they do it?" Flora asks, "the girls at work who go to analysts. I don't understand it. I can't even buy a blouse at the end of the week on my salary." Magazines have to be proofread before they go on sale in the drug stores. Fifty-five dollars a week is tops, Flora tells you, even if you've got a Columbia degree.

Flora takes a quart bottle of Ruppert beer out of the refrigerator. "I keep having dreams, Zus. Last night I dreamt I was in a tunnel, a subway tunnel, I think. A train came rushing toward me. It's phallic, I know, but it must have more meaning. Oh, I'd like to get at the inside of those meanings. I keep thinking, those lucky girls, they can stretch out on a couch, just lay back and talk, say everything that comes into their head. God it must be wonderful! I can feel it!—But you know, Zus, I shudder sometimes when I think of all the girls in publishing in New York. I think they're the ones who rush off to the psychoanalysts. What are they after in the printed word? And that includes me! Who's left to have the babies? Do you know what I think? We all want to be artists. God, what a curse the legend of the artist put on us poor people from Chicago. An artist is free the way people are really supposed to be free, he expresses himself the way people are really supposed to express themselves— and the expression is understood. That's an idea you know, and not a little one. I think analysis must be delicious, really delicious!" But not on $55.00 a week less tax deductions, social security, phone bill, lunches, subway fare.

"If I had the money I'm sure I would go, Zus. I can understand how it must be an addiction for some people. But how do you pick out a doctor that you feel will *understand?* Word of mouth? A name out of the telephone book? Alice is taking her analysis now. You should hear her rave about it. I think every one of the girls I've met since I came to New York is in it. And the men too, such weak, poor, little, frightened boys who can't get over their mothers. Their glubby talk sickens me sometimes. Michael used to lock himself in his room and scream. Can you understand that? Eddie has to drink himself crazy, blubbering. Where do you find a husband in New York? God, sometimes I think Illinois is the original Garden of Eden. None of this went on there. Why? Was it so carefully hidden? Or maybe we just didn't know enough to see it all." You listen, opening the quart bottle of Ruppert. "I don't know what I expect from analysis, Zus. I guess what the other girls do, a sense of belonging, an authoritative voice that will listen. You don't feel so alone then, senselessly drifting in and out of Italian restaurants. It's no joke when they talk about the aloneness of New York. Zus, you should have seen the girl's rooming house I lived in off of Lexington Avenue when I first came to New York. Dozens of girls in tiny little rooms, dressing up at night to eat alone at Bickford's or an Italian restaurant where no one but girls like themselves ate. I'd like to try analysis, just to see if there is something inside of me that I should know about. You should see me at night alone in this room staring up at that mobile. Round and round it goes. Then the dreams begin. All those flashes of fear about what's going to happen to my life. If an analyst can stop that, he can have my money."

But isn't it just a natural anxiety to wonder about life? "Natural! Normal! What do you have to do to be *in?* Be like my mother, losing her personality, going down through the years in Illinois with a sweet, old-fashioned smile on her face. Our energy has to be used up! And God knows I have energy. What's a city like New York for except to use up our energy? But the awful joke is that it doesn't give you half a chance. That's why I think the girls come here in droves. To use up their energy. And then when they get here? Nothing, nothingness, oh such an emptiness. One or two dates, a one and only cocktail at the Algonquin, a concert at Town Hall. You go to bed or you don't go to bed with a man. Most of the sex in New York is with frightened men. They don't know how to be free in bed, just glubb. You don't get a chance to use up your energy. And then you learn about psychoanalysis. It doesn't take long. All you need is one luncheon date with a girl at work and you'll hear enough talk to last you for months. But then you ask yourself, am I any healthier? My energy, Zus, what's going to happen to it? Talk can't use it up. Dreams can't use it up. Going to bed with a man doesn't help. Where am I being carried to? I'm not getting any younger. That's what a girl keeps saying to herself once she passes twenty-five. I know . . . marriage. But *real marriage* is like *real life*, you don't have one without the other. And you need something in this crazy cold, where-you-have-to-be city."

The beer is warm now. The mobile spins from the draft of the open window. Outside is Horatio Street, a street of renovated one-room studios. The Hudson River is only a few blocks away but huge docks hide it. The quietest sound in all New York is the lapping of the water against the docks, the sound of the writing on a wall on West Street. Cherrie loves Jon. Pablo loves Nola. Ismael loves Matilda.

If God Makes You Pretty

IT WAS THE HAPPIEST DAY OF HER LIFE, NO DOUBT ABOUT
that. Other days had been happy but this was the happiest. Now her
problem was to decide what kind of a wedding to have. He had
finally proposed, putting an end to her worries. And he had such a
lot of money.

Ilse bounced up from the sofa unable to contain so many ideas in
her head at once. The most important thing was to plan for the wedding. Where to have it, how soon, *who* or was it *whom* to invite?
And her friends, what would they say? Another problem. Her
marriage would certainly take her into a new world, that vast limestone marqueed world west of Central Park.

So many problems for such a happy day. Music they would have.
She loved music! And whisky, of course. He could afford everything! She could even wear white, walk down a rose-petaled aisle,
her eyes sad with the violins. This was a day worth waiting for!

Ilse had to talk to somebody on the telephone. Why not to Sarah?

"Hello Sarah, this is Ilse. Yes, I'm so happy. I can't believe it.
This afternoon. This very afternoon. On a Sunday afternoon. I
don't know yet. Soon though. I want to be married soon. And I'm
going to have babies, lots of babies. Oh, I want babies. He's so nice,
isn't he? Yes, come over Sarah. We'll have something at the house
tonight."

Nothing more to say to Sarah. The poor girl wanted to get married herself. That was the only way to get something out of this crazy city. The ballet was nice, the opera, the theater, concerts, smoking cigarettes during the intermission, talking, laughing, moving gracefully through the crowds, knowing you were wearing the right clothes, in style, alive, that was wonderful, but then you always had to go back to work in the morning. Always the bed, the sheets, the pillow waiting for you and you had to catch a little sleep so that you could make enough money to buy the dresses to wear to the ballet, the opera, the theater. Stupid! Tiring! No, let the man work, let his button factory bring her money. She had had enough of work. Oh, she would dress, she would show those bitches on 57th Street, those whores who stood in front of her all day long, "Look to this, Miss, this doesn't lay right, *change it!*" Then to smile again, favors, oh the bitches! Her fingers wouldn't sew anymore. Let somebody else make their clothes. What shops they had on 57th Street, like nowhere else in the world. And they paid girls like her less than the elevator operators. Oh what a dirty world. She would get back at them. Yes, yes, YES! she wanted to scream when he asked her to marry. It was such a happy day.

Who else could she call? Charolette? No, Charolette would be too jealous. Edith, yes, Edith was already married. She wouldn't upset her feelings.

"Hello Edith, this is Ilse. Yes, today. He asked me today. I'm so happy. He loves me and I love him and we love each other. It's so wonderful. Tonight—I'll give a little party. Nothing, just a few friends. Please come."

Alex would be angry, hurt, unhappy. Nobody should be unhappy today. Why didn't she marry Alex? He could give her as much as Fred. What silly names these Americans had, Fred. Who could be named Fred? Her husband, the man she loved, why did his name have to be Fred? David, Michael, so many beautiful names in the world. Her baby she would name Saul. Should she call Alex? No, he would phone her. He didn't know yet. He would phone and say, I have two tickets for the ballet tonight, would you like to go? And she would have to say, I can't go Alex, I'm engaged to be married, not formally but I accepted today. There might be tears. People cried on such occasions. Why did Alex have to be so persistent? He was a nice boy but he couldn't move big enough socially. He didn't stand straight enough. Talk forward enough. He didn't act like the men she saw at the uptown parties. The men had height, such clothes, such beautiful manners. Poor Alex.

What about the party tonight? She promised so many people. Who should come? Only people who made her happy. Some of her friends might object to her marrying a rich boy. They were so progressive. But everybody wanted to marry rich. It was the only way of getting out. She could work until she was eighty and have nothing. Life was so sad. She would make Fred happy. He loved her! In two short busy months he had found out that he loved her, wanted her more than any other woman in the world. It was such a wonderful feeling to be loved. Where else could she find such a love? This America was a wonderful country. She did the right thing when the camps were liberated. Asking to be sent here. The Americans had so much. The best, always the best. What food they put into tins!

Corned beef, Pepsi-Cola, rye bread, some smoked whitefish, salami, that would be enough for a party. Marta would be home soon. She could help prepare the food. Beer they should have. And there was that reduced Italian red wine. But this was Sunday. The liquor shops were closed. Marta, oh Marta, her wonderful sister, what would she say? She didn't know yet. It had come as such a surprise. She didn't expect a proposal herself. And women are supposed to know such things. It's in you from birth, from the beginning of time. But she was quick enough to say yes. And how he kissed her. He had such a big mouth. She wondered if he knew that she was a virgin. She looked so sophisticated! He probably thought that no girl could have come out of the concentration camps a virgin, clean, but she would show him. He was getting a virgin. What a bold way of thinking! But it was important to be a virgin. It proved that you loved your husband. He would be the only one. Would she ever have a lover? The women at the shop talked so freely about lovers. They seemed to be like pieces of chocolate in a shop window. But a real lover, no, why think about it now? Marta, oh what would she say? Her darling sister would be happy, happy for her. Fred was a nice boy.

The door buzzer. Marta was downstairs. Ilse pressed the button to release the door. Marta was on the first landing now. Soon she would be at the door. How should she tell her the news? Blurt it out? No, that would be no good. Marta would know by her eyes. Her eyes shone like a girl in love. She loved Fred and he loved her and they loved one another. Oh, it was such a wonderful feeling.

"Hello Ilse. I'm so tired." Marta stretched out on the couch and closed her eyes.

"What's wrong, Marta?" Ilse asked, disturbed.

"Nothing. It's such a horrible day. The sun makes me feel weak. I would like to go away. Do you think I could get a job at a summer camp?"

Ilse had forgotten how hot the day was. Marta was so miserable. What could she do? Tell her now, the news would make the day seem less hot. Marta would be happy for her.

"Marta, I have some news for you."

"Good, what is it?"

"Fred was up this afternoon."

"How come you didn't go out with him?"

"He only stopped up for a few minutes. He had to join his family at a wedding."

"I'll bet it was a big wedding. Everybody he knows has money. How do people become rich? Oh, it's so hot."

"Marta, he—"

"You don't have to say any more!" Marta leapt up from the couch. She took her sister around and they both started crying. Ilse was the first to stop crying.

"We were alone in the flat. I wasn't sure that he was going to ask me. I felt so alone. I was frightened, Marta. Should I say yes or say no."

"You said the right thing, Ilse. Believe me, boy you said the right thing."

"He loves me, Marta."

"That makes it a hundred times better."

"We're going to have a big wedding. A supper for a hundred people. I won't have to work anymore, Marta. No more work."

Marta stretched out on the couch again. She looked at her baby sister. Ilse was still a baby. When do women become old? Ilse had the body to catch a rich husband. What breasts. And a figure. A model's figure. A rich husband would be proud of her. Rich men never married skinny ugly women. Only voluptuous women. Women with big breasts. But poor women had big breasts too. Figure out the world. How did Fred come into the house? No, there was no way of figuring these things out. They just happened. If people knew, then there would be an end to life. No more excitement. But some people were smarter than the others. They knew how to get their way. How did Fred get his button factory, maybe Fred had a friend. She and Ilse and Fred and the friend could live door to door in a big house on West End. It was no good for her and Ilse to separate. They depended too much on one another. Ilse would be lost. The crazy way the world moved since the camp. She would be alone now in the big apartment. Where to get the money to pay the rent? God, she didn't want to give it up to take a furnished room.

"Marta!"

"What is it, Ilse?"

"I invited some people over for tonight. I forgot all about it. We need some salami, corned beef, beer and bread."

"A party so soon?"

"I talked to Sarah and Edith. They're coming up. And then people always come up on Sunday. I had to tell somebody. I was all alone in the house. Nobody to tell the news to."

"All right. We'll go downstairs and do some shopping."

Ilse looked at Marta as they walked down the stairs. Marta wasn't as happy as she expected her to be. Marta was the oldest sister. She should have waited for her to marry first. But who can wait now? She might not meet another Fred. He was so anxious to get married. He wanted a woman for himself. That was a terrible way to think about marriage. But she could feel it in him. Marta would have to wait until a man desired her. She hoped it wouldn't be a long wait. Her sister was pretty. If God makes you pretty then you have nothing to worry about.

Marta opened the front door. The sun was shining bright. Ilse blinked. It was the first time she was out today. Oh, the Sundays to come! The expensive suits she would wear. She and Fred walking through Washington Square Park, taking lunch at the Fifth Avenue Hotel. Sunday would no longer mean Monday and sewing in linings on two hundred dollar suits!

"Where do you want to buy the salami?" Marta asked.

"At David's. It's ten cents cheaper on the pound."

"Good. We'll get everything at David's."

The two sisters walked down the street to the delicatessen on the corner, the sun shining brightly on their heads. Ilse's heart was full of happiness. She would give a real party tonight. The sun was shining just for her! She looked at her sister Marta, expecting her to be smiling in the sun, too. Marta looked so sad. What was wrong? Oh! The apartment! Who would live in the apartment now? And so much rent to pay! She didn't think of it until now. Why was life so complicated?

"How many pounds of salami do you think will be enough?" Marta asked Ilse.

"Two pounds. Eddie eats like a cow," Ilse said, on the verge of tears.

"We'll make a potato salad and have lots of beer. We need at least eight bottles," Marta suggested.

Ilse tried to say something about the party but she couldn't. Her eyes were full of tears. She was crying on the street.

"Ilse, darling sister, what's wrong?" Marta asked.

"I'm so happy," Ilse sobbed. "I'm so happy. Marta, do you think it will be all right if I paid half the rent on the apartment until you find a husband?"

The Movers

THEY WERE IN THE GROCERY STORE TOGETHER. HER mother had on a white apron over her blue cotton dress. The one she always wore to wait on trade. Anne was helping her mother, pretending to be a super saleslady. Only this afternoon there wasn't much business. It was a game they played whenever she came home for a visit. Because they both knew that when she was younger the most terrible thing in the world for her was to spend long hours in the store, weighing up the potatoes, even taking the empty cases of milk downstairs to the damp cellar, stocking the shelves with cans, being nice to the customers. She used to yell at home: "No, Ma, I don't want to go into the store!" And her mother would say: "But the store gives you a living, doesn't it? Eat and sleep! But where would you be without the store?"

"How are you getting along?" Anne remembered her mother asking.

"All right, Ma."

"And Hy?"

"He's all right."

"When do you think you'll have a baby?"

"A baby—?"

"Why not? Why not? Wouldn't you like a baby?"

"Yes, Ma, I'd like a baby. I'd like a big house, too. I'd like everything th at every girl who went to school with me now has. But—"

"But what?"

"But—"

A customer came into the store just then. And the conversation was forgotten. That was the last time she had seen her mother. Three months later she died. And now she faced Hy for what might be the last time.

All morning she had been preparing herself. By walking, thinking, going into the shops on Fifth Avenue, fingering the imported woolens, French handbags, thrusting herself into the perfumed world of women who carried their wealth on their backs. If she had the money she would have liked to have bought a new cotton on 14th Street. But she didn't have the money and a new dress couldn't give her the lift of arms slid into a fresh crisp cotton. Not now, for the coldness had come.

"You dirty son of a bitch!"

Anne heard the words flung across the length of the long narrow room. How many times had she heard women called sons of bitches? The angry voices coming up the airshaft. On the stairway she looked at her neighbors, the Italian women in cotton wrap-arounds going down to the Bleecker Street market, coming up the dim hallway with twisted loaves of French bread. Sons of bitches, the men called them. They fought, the anger building as violently as the quarrels her parents had had, the high pitched screams of her mother. Once her father threw a pot at her mother's head and it missed, landing dumbly on the kitchen floor. How ashamed they both looked at one another. She promised herself, buried under the covers when her mother's screams wouldn't end, that she wouldn't quarrel if she ever married. How wonderful it was, she thought then, that she could know what to do with her life.

When Anne didn't answer, Hy shouted again, "You dirty son of a bitch!"

And then Anne said as simply as she could, "Please, Hy, let's not make a great big fight out of this. We've had too many fights already."

"No fights! You dirty whore!"

"Hy!"

"Don't Hy me! She goes out and lays some dirty bastard and now she Hys me!"

Anne kept still. Not sure of what to say, not at all certain she could say anything. The distance was her doing, the river that ran between them. She could have kept silent about the two or three men she had gone to bed with, their names almost forgotten now. She could have even invented a lie about last night. But she told him the truth. And the truth was too much for him to live with. Who was the man she had gone to bed with last night? Stayed all night with. She couldn't even remember his name, only his voice, soft, patronizing, buying her a beer on 13th Street. And why did she go to bed with him? In Delaware they warned her against marrying a painter. But what could they know about a painter? They only said in chorus: "Don't be a fool, he won't be able to make a penny for you." They married. The sun didn't turn black. Flowers didn't wilt in shop windows. The world took no recognition. Only she had to care. Where was the man who talked straight out of a philosophy book on the beach in Delaware where he had dug his hands into the sand, talking so beautifully about the non-existence of God, of his early life, the winter afternoons when the sun did strange things to the snow, the house he escaped from and the friendless labyrinth he had to solve before he could set himself up as a painter—of the dreams he lived in to be published in a handsomely printed future brochure of a retrospective show, saying, ". . . my life then was the waiting-in period, the agony the pregnant mother feels before she utters her last final scream and forces into the world a miracle, a human, weeping, alive, destined with a purpose. . ." When they married, he boasted, "Anne and I were married by a JP who only asked us to believe in the state and not in God."

"You know this means a separation," Hy said when Anne didn't answer. "I wouldn't live with you for another ten minutes in this house."

Let him go, was all Anne could feel. She didn't try to stop him with words when he turned to leave the narrow room they had lengthened into a studio by smashing down one of the dividing walls. He wanted to be free. Free for what? It's a terrible thing to live with a painter but not for the reasons her friends had poured on her head. They always had money, from his GI checks, her jobs, they had never been without food, beer. But there had never been love between them. Did he imagine there had been? She did, she knew, she did! It was love until he began to swallow her up. He needed her to feed on. He had no one in the world. And he was afraid. It made her afraid when she found him out. Betty drank whisky. Lucille beer. Pat gin. She could have gone off on Friday night drunks, some of the wives did, she knew. Or she could have sewn clothes, knitted, made leather sandals, the other wives of the painters she knew did. But she married him to be his wife and that's all she knew or wanted.

On their Sunday dates on the beach in Delaware he had talked about New York, pointing north toward the skyscrapers as though he were Balboa first viewing the Pacific. He sketched in the sand a drawing he had once made of Fifth Avenue from a hill in Central Park, the green trees poking up, the little swirl of a lake, the towers of limestone. The tide came and washed away the towers. He laughed, saying, "Those are the bastards who'll have to buy my paintings." When she married him in Delaware he told her what it would be like being married to a painter. But how could he have known? He made it a wild dream. The little girl in her went out with the tide. Coming from Delaware to New York! The room on Bleecker Street up five flights. Outside of one window you could see the rooftops of the Village. He showed her the courtyards on Barrow Street. The chess players in Washington Square. The bearded men with "lunatic fringes" as he called the beards who painted pictures in cold loft studios. The wild dream was simple. He would paint. And the world would crowd up the five puffing flights of stairs, it would all come to him as the Pacific had rolled toward Balboa.

At first it was a dream. New York is first a dream, then a breaking headache that makes you want to run toward open fields. One night when they walked from Bleecker Street across the Bowery, through the narrow streets of Italian restaurants to the Brooklyn Bridge, looking up at the black towers against the black steel webs that leapt toward lower Manhattan, she could see that New York was linked, people to the buildings, life to the electric light bulbs. It wasn't as he had told her, that you had to fight the city as though windmills everywhere spun you like grains of wheat. Cities don't happen overnight. They grow because people grow. How else could such a city rise on a rocky island? And how could he grow unless he planted himself in roots other than endless bravuras of his revolt from his family. He grew by draining her. And she was willing to let him win subtle arguments, even turn her taste in reading, keep her working, wondering at night about babies, bringing money from dreary office jobs, as though he had by marrying her magically become arbiter over his mother and father, brothers and sisters, all the relatives who taunted him. She believed in him as a painter. His canvases were solid, the colors laid on with profound attention. The infrequent friends who came to the house liked his work. But she wasn't willing to go all the way with him as he was with her.

Anne heard the door slam. So now the neighbors had heard her called a son of a bitch. Soon their friends would know. Not their friends but his friends. She had made no friends. How? At the office jobs behind clattering typewriters? On Bleecker Street with its Italian accent? The two, three men she had gone to bed with as the roots of a tree grope underground for water?

In the morning Hy called. "We've got a few things to say to one another. Let's say them quick and fast."

"What do you have to say?" Anne asked.

"The first thing is that we're getting a divorce. I don't want to live with you. I couldn't stand to be in the same room with you."

Anne thought of hanging up. But let the words come.

"I figured it out last night. I think I'm the one who's got the say in this matter. I'll give you the apartment and I'm taking the furniture. You seem to be pretty good at shifting for yourself. You'll be able to pick up some furniture. I'm going to start looking for a bigger place beginning today. As soon as I find a loft I'll have the movers move the stuff out. How does that sound?"

Sound? She knew how it sounded. He had brought her naked to New York. And he was going to leave her naked in New York.

"All right," Anne said. "I don't want to argue. Whatever you want to do we'll do." He had always hated Bleecker Street. But where could they live? Not in a skylight studio. Not in five rooms. The rents were fantastic unless you could find a floor-through railroad flat. And the railroad flats had been all parceled out long before they came to New York. "The squeeze is on," he had once said about the shortage of apartments. "Somebody will have to get out of the city and then we'll have our pick of an apartment." But nothing ever happened except the wasted Thursday mornings chasing the ads in the *Villager*. And one morning they got the idea of smashing down one of the dividing walls and they created a long narrow studio room. Maybe that's why he never considered Bleecker Street home. But home is where you live out your life. And your life is always with you. He would find a loft. He had to. Because he still considered a painting important, a studio, but not himself, not the way he imagined.

On Wednesday Anne saw that Hy had come to the house while she was at work and had picked up a change of clothes. He didn't leave a note, just an open dresser drawer. The phone rang just as she was about to prepare supper for herself.

"I found a place," he told her. "A loft on Third Avenue."

"When will the movers be around?" Anne asked.

"Probably next Saturday."

"You'll have to pack everything."

"I know," he told her. "I'll be over Monday to tie the paintings together and to box the books in cartons." Twice they had moved. And each time the paintings came down off the rack and were tied together, stacked against the walls. On the back of the paintings she saw the prices he had written down, $500, $1,000, one huge canvas he marked $1,500. A few people had bought his paintings. But not for $500, nor for a $1,000. Fifty dollars, some for $25.00, even $15.00. With the sale of one painting they bought a double-size bed, layers of springs, cotton, horse hair. What did the buyers look for when they studied one of Hy's paintings? She never had the chance to sit in a twenty-five foot living room on Fifth Avenue high above the park and see one of Hy's paintings displayed on a blue-green wall, cocktails resting on a marble-top table, all the eyes staring, full of the wonderment people use to look at paintings. What had he lived thirty-six years for? Not to hang a painting on a blue-green wall. Not to quarrel with her because she happened to go to bed with a stranger. For what did his life take shape making him the only one of himself? Wouldn't it be easier and better if he would come to the house on Monday and they would kiss and go to bed, their naked bodies not so naked?

On Monday Hy came and took his paintings down from the rack he had built against one long side of the room and on Friday he phoned to tell Anne that the movers would come Saturday at 11 a.m.

Anne didn't want to face the movers, see the flat emptied, stripped. She got up early and left the apartment, turning from Bleecker into Seventh Avenue toward Washington Square and then decided as she crossed the Square to walk up Fifth Avenue into the mobs of people. At 59th Street, the shops came to an end. Fifth Avenue stretched white and marble, a safe deposit vault, great steel doors guarded by men in white stiff collars chained to opening taxicab doors. This was one part of the world he had talked about in Delaware. "Those are the bastards who'll have to buy my paintings." In these buildings? Anne looked up at the limestone sheet of windows ending in ivy growing out of wooden boxes. How many windows would buy a painting? How alike the windows were. "Don't put your eggs in other people's baskets," her mother always told her customers. Buildings white. Park green. Sky blue. People walking on two legs. Why didn't he ever paint people walking on two legs, the sky blue, the park green, the buildings white? The movers were going down the wooden stairs, the neighbors sticking their heads out of the kitchen doors. "Is the apartment taken?" A vacant apartment! "Is the apartment taken?" "No, my wife is staying, my wife is staying." Oh? Oh? Oh? Now they would know who she was when she walked up the stairs at night. And then a wild thought occurred to her. In New York most people lived with two, three roofs over their heads and here on Fifth Avenue, Park Avenue, even in the Village, people lived with ten, twenty roofs over their head. And on Bleecker Street she had one roof over her head.

The door was locked when Anne returned. When she opened it,

the empty kitchen, painted a flat green with the smudge where the medicine cabinet had been pulled off the wall, the stripped cupboards standing open, made her run, sick and ready to burst, over to the studio couch that opened into a bed. Her clothes lay scattered on the couch but in the empty sun-drenched room they looked more like a pile of rags. The movers had carted everything away, pots, pans, dishes, even the kitchen table, chairs, the medicine cabinet off the wall. The window blinds were up and the sun coming off the top of the brick wall facing the flat lit up the dust on the floor where the bed had been uprooted. The books were off the wall and out of the room. The movers had left behind the empty dry smell of burlap. He didn't leave a single painting. Not one painting out of three married years. She thought of making that one of the conditions when they agreed to separate, for some of the paintings were as much of her as they were of him. The walls hung bare stripped of his reds and blues. He tried to work inside of a color, he had always told her, and as a result his canvases bounced light one to the other hung the length of their room. And she sat naked for him on the double bed while he tried to make the nakedness come together on canvas. That she should have insisted on. One of her nudes. But she couldn't ask him for a painting, nor for anything else. Let him think he was free.

Anne got up from the studio couch and did what she had to do first. She swept the floor and gathered up the dirt the movers had left. Then she covered the smudge left by the medicine cabinet with an old calendar. She didn't know how to fill in the space left by the double bed. She tried shoving the couch over, then moved the big chair they had bought at an auction sale for $1.50 to where the couch had been, falling tired into the chair. She listened to the silence of the two rooms he had left her, the quarrels imbedded in the walls, an echo unable to lose itself in bigness. Babies have such a happy smiling innocence, such trust. Hadn't she delivered herself over to him like a baby clutching at its mother's skirt? Once she lay in bed watching him paint, wondering how his putting paint on the white canvas and her going off to 47th Street every day made them belong to New York. "Why don't we go with the Jonas's up to the top of the

Beekman Tower some night?" she asked him. "What's up there?" he asked. "The skyline, the East River, you can get a perfect view of the UN Building, Ralph said there's no place like it in New York." But he refused to go because the management asked you to wear a necktie. What was he doing now on Third Avenue with all of his pride and paints and brushes? For the first time in three years she lay down to sleep alone, opening the couch into the hard cotton mattress.

Until Friday Anne lived with the big chair and the studio couch. On Friday afternoon she attended the auction sale at Kaliski and Gabay. A Victorian mirror came up, a towering mirror framed in gold, a marble base that could fill the emptiness of the flat. But the bidding began at $35.00 and rose to $85.00. Anne sat back and waited for the bargains to come. Chairs followed andirons, settees, chaise lounges, bookcases, tables, chests, bric-a-brac, bushels filled with kitchen utensils. Anne bought one well-stuffed bushel filled with pots, pans, knives, dishes, salt shakers, heavy spoons, forks, a coffee percolator, salad plate. Then she bought a stuffed club chair with real down cushions for only $4.50. Finally the bed she had noticed on Thursday came up, a huge bed with a carved headboard of velvety material, a vast bed but she knew it would fill the space he had emptied. Anne listened for the opening bid. The bed might bring a lot of money. She wanted the bed, the deep springs, the custom mattress, soft and thick. "Do I hear $5.00—" Five dollars only! Anne waved her hand. "Five is bid. Do I have six, six is bid, seven—" Anne waved her hand again and the bed was hers for $8.00. Immediately after the bed, Anne bought a box of books the titles unseen, a pine bookcase and a wrought iron lamp, bidding $1.50 for the lamp.

The movers came again to the flat on Monday evening. This time Anne waited for the movers. And after they left she spent the night arranging and rearranging the furniture she had bought at the auction sale and it wasn't until the wrought iron lamp threw shadows she had never seen before that she felt the room belonged to her.

The phone lay silent. Her old friends, rather, their old friends didn't call. How had they shown it at the RKO, a man drifting off

into space with an acetylene torch in his hand. Didn't she often feel
that if she were ever left alone in New York she would swerve, a
body lost beyond pull. Hy made her feel that way. Hy and the
brownstones in the West 80's that had frightened her at first, the row
on row of flats on Second Avenue, busses piling up on Fifth, 34th
Street shrieked. Where were the French restaurants, the posters of
Nice on the wall? Why didn't they ever walk in Central Park? The
trees weren't real enough for him! The smallness. The friends gathering to mercilessly attack those absent from the bottled beer. How
many times now had he made her the butt of the conversation?
His not seeing her nakedness. Her breasts were up. Her belly flat.
Down below was the warmth she had pressed on him and that he
took, as though the taking was it. What was *it*, nothing except that
she thought she could live with him, love him, that would be enough;
in-between would be the city spreading out, rising up, that they
talked about over endless bottles of beer—the tables of painters full
of talk, the loud table of talk unlistened to. Did anyone ever remember what had been said? Never did they go to the names talked
about—Town Hall, the Night Court, Chinese food on Mott Street,
the Oriental cabarets on Allen where men danced together clasping
handkerchiefs. Drown your life in bottles of beer.

On Thursday night Anne rode the Seventh Avenue bus past the
dark Chelsea streets and got off in the lighted blaze of Times Square.
A newsdealer told her where to find Town Hall.

The doors of Town Hall were open, a poster announcing a piano
recital. A man in a dinner jacket smiled at Anne and shoved a
student admission ticket in her hand. Anne looked at the ticket and
saw she only had to pay 60¢ to sit through the recital. Bargains everywhere! An usher led her down the aisle to an orchestra seat. At
eight-thirty the slim young man of the poster came out on the stage
in a stiff black-tailed tuxedo, bowing slightly to the audience. He
seemed to suck his breath as he turned to face the black piano on the
bare bright stage. He held still for a minute above the keys and Anne
saw Hy staring at a white canvas, the brush wavering. Often she
wanted to ask him, just what do you think about, Hy, when you
begin a painting. But some questions are never asked. The hands

came down and struck music Anne had never heard before, Schumann's *Fantastiestucke, Op. 12* traveling to the far wall of the audience of empty seats, the long rows of seats turned up. Striking notes, repeating another man's music. Ushers, ticket takers, curtain pullers, why—who was the man who gave her a student admission ticket? Why was the player on the stage striking the notes? Who were the people in the audience who would wait for him in the reception room, offering congratulations. The same sheet of limestone windows? Did he have a wife and was she in the audience listening? But wasn't she always proud to tell the girls at the office, my husband is a painter, a fine artist and she always had to explain what she meant by a *fine artist.* "He paints pictures, the kind you see in a museum." "Oh, that kind." "That kind," she would say and then prepare herself for the next question: "Does he make a living at it?" "No, he doesn't make a living at it—but he does it anyway!" But if they were to ask her why he does it anyway, she couldn't say. Who else but an artist's wife could know the timeless days that weren't tabulated, black pencil crosses on a calendar. Oils drying into lasting shapes. The world of possibility looming like the easel that meant so much to the western world, guarded by five-foot walls, policemen with guns. The forms that grew silently like a sleeping baby in so many dimensions on the linen canvas. And her own life that shrank away into a color enveloped by toneless blues.

At night from her down-cushion chair under the wrought iron lamp, Anne could hear the Christopher Street ferry sounding its warning blast everytime the gates clanged shut ready for the crossing to Hoboken. One night Anne followed the sound of the throated horn and boarded a ferry ready to leave for New Jersey. The ferry churned out of its long narrow dock. New York looked low and flat on its western side. The shoreline pulled away, dots of lights, red tips in the sky, the murky, misty pile of lower Manhattan. Anne leaned against the railing surprised by the breadth of the Hudson. So much water forming the island. A freighter pushed past 23rd Street, its hulk looming large against the tugboats. She could make out Bleecker Street by the lights of the terraces of the big apartment house on the corner of Christopher and Bleecker.

"Recognize it?" Anne heard.

"What—?" she asked, turning.

It was Hy. A flush on her face.

"The house?"

"Just the block it's in."

"Alone?" he asked.

Anne didn't answer. She turned back to the railing. It seemed that the ferry was heading straight for the freighter. Brrrrumph, the freighter sounded. Wasn't it a law of the sea that the ferry had to wait for the freighter to pass? Men sailing out into the Atlantic. The sea made you aware that people lived elsewhere, that life somehow went on. She wished the ferry would stop in the middle of the Hudson and let the freighter sail past.

"They won't hit," Hy said.

"No," Anne said.

"What're you going to Hoboken for?" he asked.

Anne didn't answer. Nor could she begin to tell him about the nights away from the room, alone, the Second Avenue bus that had taken her to the Hungarian restaurants on 79th Street, the *brau* houses, windows of paprika, embroidered blouses hand-stitched in Europe. Or the Night Court as one old man stood alone before the Judge, saying, "Your Honor, I'm seventy-two years old. I have no relatives, no friends, no income, nobody in the world. I want you to put me away where people will look after me." And the Eighth Avenue bus that had carried her into Harlem past the sad side streets, blocks of tenement flats. She wondered why great crowds didn't gather to cheer the men on top of the evacuated tenements as they pried loose the rotting bricks and sent them tumbling in dust. Steam shovels digging vast pits. A great swinging steel ball. Housing projects going up. A new face rising. The world doesn't completely belong to the devil. But a block further more stiff black buildings. Picasso, Modigliani, Cezanne, glowed at her from the walls of the Museum of Modern Art. Downstairs John Barrymore played *Jekyll and Hyde*. And she flinched a little at the loud laughter of those who had to announce their presence in the auditorium.

Such smug faces that made you wonder a little what you were doing with your own life, voices that made it a practice to be exactly right on everything.

One Sunday the 8th Street crosstown bus carried her into the Lower East Side and she bought a jar of dill pickles and a flowered vase off a pushcart. She walked as far as East Broadway and saw the baby carriages lining the park benches, everywhere she saw baby carriages, Italian, Yiddish, Chinese, Puerto Rican, mothers. She heard no complaints in Seward Park. Life has to be taken care of. The young mothers talking about the growing waistlines of their husbands, the price of meat, the mountains. "I don't mind staying in the city for the summer. Really, I like New York in the summer. Maybe next year we'll go away." She watched boys with *yarmulkas* safely clamped on their heads playing stickball. Old bearded Hasidim in black round beaver hats swinging their grandchildren high into the air of Seward Park. The unbelievably happy faces of Chinese babies. Then she walked down Cherry Street attracted by the low-hanging Manhattan Bridge and wondered when the steam shovels would come to smash into dust the old-law flats that looked swallowed up by their own filth. All these things she had done alone, going out of her room on Bleecker into the streets as though the city were a museum.

"You know," Hy said, "you can take the ferry back again from Hoboken to Barclay Street."

"We did make that ride once," Anne said.

"How's the apartment coming?"

"I bought some things at Kaliski."

"Betty asks why you don't call her."

"Why doesn't she call me?"

"That's her business," Hy said. "I talked to the lawyer. The divorce papers have been filed. Ralph and Griffin are going to be the witnesses."

"Oh—" Anne said. She had forgotten that somebody would have to be a witness against her. Weren't women once stoned? Didn't Hawthorne write a book about a capital A? How had Hy broadcast the verdict? The tables of beer must have her sleeping with every man who could get into line. She knew the way it was, the smallness, the coldness. The ferry passed safely under the freighter.

"When will the divorce be?" Anne asked.

"The lawyer will have to get a calendar date."

"I don't have to show up?"

"I don't know."

The railroad tower of Hoboken directed the ferry into the slip.

"Going for a beer?" Hy asked.

"No," Anne said, "I'm taking the next boat back."

"OK," Hy said, "I'll let you know when more news comes."

Anne watched Hy turn into the Hoboken streets. The coldness had really come. It was the first time she had run into him outside of the house. He made her feel as though she had an enemy in the city.

The next day after work Anne walked into a bar on 44th Street and ordered a martini. The glass felt cold and wet in her hand. The martini was a luxury, almost the price of supper, but the cold gin made her warm. The damp salt air of the Hudson had stayed with her all through the night. She couldn't sleep listening to the ships sounding. A mist had probably come up. And the ships had to warn one another of their presence. They tugged on their horns. Only martinis were left now to announce one's presence. The world grew with the gin, the eyes opened. What if she and Hy could get drunk together, gin drunk, and talk to one another as the ships spoke, the loud thrugging, the sound that entered into your whole body. Wasn't the entire world frequency waves, what else were the waves of coldness between her and Hy? Resonance, no resonance, lights, water, air, smoke, stars, the sun, her own body with its de- mands ending in a ting. The streets gave themselves up to her. She walked out of the bar into 44th Street, the fading light caught between the buildings, cabs rushing toward Grand Central Sta- tion, the Algonquin sign important, leather chairs around soft voices, the haze forming that she liked so much, as though all the people on the sidewalk were on the great stage of the Radio City Theater.

Plink! nickels dropped into the coin box of the Seventh Avenue bus, voices behind saying, "Two hundred, three hundred a week, and you can spend the summers at Fire Island, East Hampton. . . ." The bus passed the great misty shadows forming between the garment center buildings, reddish streets, the sun leveling somewhere far beyond Penn Station. Streets of mountains, shops and shops of mink tails. Anne looked out of the bus window at the sun reddening the brick. The big red sun. *Fair as the moon, clear as the sun and terrible as an army with banners.* Didn't she want to love! Love was a command. But it was the command of a sky red with the sun, the sun falling into the dark dusk. The big red sun. The big doors of the bus opening. Bleecker and Seventh Avenue. How big and how small the sun can make you feel.

On Sunday morning the sun came through the drawn shade. Anne planned an outing all by herself to Jacob Riis Park. It might be too cold to go in swimming but the beach would be warm. The Seventh Avenue express train took her to Flatbush Avenue and there she caught a bus for the park. Umbrellas dotted the beach. The wind carried the surf high above the shore line. Anne stretched out her blanket, holding down the ends with the package of ham sandwiches she brought, her slack shoes. The sun warmed her back, the nape of her neck. Then she turned to brown her face. The wind died and the surf died. Anne stood at the edge of the water letting the coldness out of her legs and then she waded into the surf, ducking her head into the gentle walls of water that broke at the end of the ocean. The water ended here where the beach became earth. It all seemed so beautifully thought out. Didn't she read somewhere that if you doubted the meaning of a broken twig then you doubted the existence of God. You only had to open your eyes to know the wonder. The afternoon passed quickly, most of it spent on the hard-packed beach, then sleeping on her back, feeling the sun turning away from the ocean. Her skin still radiated the heat of the sun when she left the beach to go into the subway and walk up the five flights of her house listening to the harsh voices behind closed doors. At the end of the hallway she saw a white envelope stuck in her door above the lock.

"I tried to see you this afternoon," the note read. No other explanation.

Anne closed the door to her flat and stretched out on her big bed. The sun had exhausted her. She turned the note over in her hand, wondering if Hy would phone. There was no way of knowing what he had been thinking these past days. Maybe if she looked at a new canvas of his, or phoned Betty, or Max. But they wouldn't say. Tomorrow Hy would look at her as though she were the whore of Babylon if he thought she had spent the day with a man. She knew his look, his eyes narrowing, as though that was the way you looked into things. You had to open your eyes. Once she tested herself sitting in Washington Square waiting for Hy. She sat and waited and looked and only saw the faded green bench in front of her with the aged Italian men in slouch hats smoking pipes. Then she raised her eyes and looked further and saw the big trees of the Square, the wholeness of people walking, the shadows and green, the yellow of the Fifth Avenue busses turning. It surprised her, how much the eye could see. But what could the eye see with its graven image alone? When had Hy ever looked at her with the feeling that provoked him to press paint down on a white canvas?

The phone rang at 11:00.

"Hello."

"Hello."

"You know who this is?" He always began with a joke.

"Yes," Anne said.

"I tried to see you this afternoon."

"I know. I saw the note."

"Were you out?"

"Yes, I went out."

"I wanted to talk to you about something. Will you be free tomorrow?"

"Yes. What about?"

"Something with the lawyer. We have to get our stories straight for the divorce."

"*Our stories straight!*" Anne said and she couldn't have been more alone than if the surf had carried her out into the cold sea.

"There's one story everybody tells the judge. Nobody pays any attention to it. But it has to be told right. The lawyer will give you a briefing on it."

"All right," Anne said, she couldn't say anything more, "come up at eight o'clock."

Anne pulled back the sheet of her great big bed. The sheet came down on top of her. The heat of the sun was still on her body. How big and how small the sun can make you feel. *We have to get our stories straight.* Before what? whom? who makes stories straight? Unbend Hy! Did he know what he had said? Or had his words lost all their meaning trying to get ahead of the days that had to follow. How quickly people sucked life dry. Outside of her window she thought of the subways running underground, the rumbling bus that had taken her into the Atlantic surf, the great steel ball smashing into the brick walls of Harlem, embroidered blouses on 79th Street, the millions of people who breathed in the elevators going up, the little Italian elevator operator in her office building who told her that in India he had hung a wet bedsheet over an open window to cool a hot humid room—the city that had taken her to bed with breasts chock-full of pregnant milk. God, who could suck the island dry.

About the Author

JULIUS HORWITZ was raised in a melting pot city, Cleveland, on a street that had practically every nationality and religion represented on it. Growing up in this exciting and—for the sensitive—stimulating atmosphere, living and playing and fighting with Jew and Catholic, Russian and Irish, Italian and Hungarian, German and Polish and Negro, he was thus, in a sense, prepared for the city of his choice, New York. He was prepared to accept it kindly and with understanding for what it was, not for what he or others wanted it to be, and he was prepared to see it and live it from the inside.

Born in 1920, Mr. Horwitz attended the Cleveland schools, went down to Ohio State, then migrated after the war to New York, where he went to Columbia and the New School, from which he has a degree. Early interested in the drama (while at Ohio State he won awards for his plays), he turned to fiction and creative reportage, publishing his first work in *Commentary*, later work there and in the *Jewish Frontier*. During his three-year Air Force service he wrote a musical play for the troops entitled *Off Limits*.

An emigre from his native town, as his parents were from Europe, fitly enough he met his wife, a Cleveland girl, in New York. At one time a "candy butcher" in a burlesque theatre, later an age and weight guesser in carnivals and state fairs, Mr. Horwitz is now devoting full time to his writing, currently working on his first novel.